TALES

WORCESTER ROYAL INFIRMARY

MIRIAM HARVEY
S.R.N.

WORCESTERSHIRE INDUSTRIAL
ARCHAEOLOGY AND LOCAL HISTORY
SOCIETY

TALES FROM WORCESTER ROYAL INFIRMARY
MIRIAM HARVEY

Published by Aspect Design 2012
Malvern, Worcestershire, United Kingdom
On behalf of
Worcestershire Industrial Archaeology and Local History Society (WIALHS)
www.worcester-wia.co.uk

Designed and Printed by Aspect Design
89 Newtown Road, Malvern, Worcs. WR14 1PD
United Kingdom
Tel: 01684 561567
E-mail: books@aspect-design.net
Website: www.aspect-design.net

Cover painting of Worcester Royal Infirmary by David Birtwhistle, with his kind permission, © 2011 David Birtwhistle

THE INFIRMARY.

Table of Contents

INTRODUCTION

WORCESTER ROYAL INFIRMARY always held a fascination for me, ever since the day in 1952 when I first set eyes on the handsome Georgian building. It had been my ambition to train as a nurse, from when I was a tiny girl, and I remember standing with my face pressed up against the hospital railings in Infirmary Walk. Gazing with admiration at the hospital, I made up my mind in that instant that this was where I would do my training.

My childhood years had been spent in Treyarnon Bay, on the north coast of Cornwall. These were the war-time years and my father was overseas serving in the Fleet Air Arm. After the war we moved to Smethwick where my grandparents lived, and I attended Holly Lodge, a well-known and forward looking grammar school. Here I was able to take my pre-nursing exams, and then applied to the School of Nursing at Worcester Royal Infirmary. I was accepted in the summer of 1954 and presented myself, with great excitement, for training in August of that year.

The welcoming homely and highly organized establishment enfolded me;

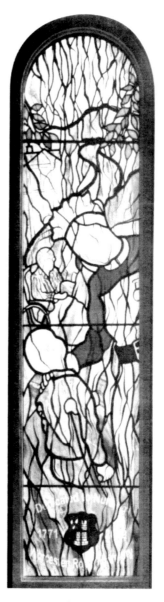

JENNY LIND CHAPEL
WINDOW

1

the sense of history was strong, and I felt so privileged to be part of this ancient family. To live and work in the Infirmary was just like being a member of an enormous extended family, with its traditions and legends. It seemed that every inch of the building had a tale to tell. As I learned more and more of the origins and history of the hospital and the characters who had gone before me who had created this wonderful establishment, it seemed to me that it was really important to record for posterity some of the tales and anecdotes of my colleagues, past and present.

In 1947 W.H.McMenemy, a pathologist at the Infirmary, wrote a highly esteemed *History of Worcester Royal Infirmary* to celebrate its 200th anniversary, but nothing has been written since then, as far as I am aware.

This collection of stories and articles is mostly of 20th Century characters and personal memories together with some of the more interesting tales of the beginnings of the old Infirmary – and the major events concerning the Castle Street hospital. Some of these articles have already been published, individually, in the annual *Newsletter of the Worcester Royal Infirmary Nurses League* over the last 15 years.

The year 2011 was the silver jubilee of the WRI Nurses League and the 240th anniversary of the opening of the Castle Street Infirmary in 1771 – and to commemorate both events and mark the work of nurses over these years, the Nurses League have installed a stained-glass window, designed by Nick Upton, in the Jenny Lind Chapel.

I hope that anyone who has ever worked at the Infirmary, or who has been a patient or visitor will find this collection of stories interesting and will enjoy reading them.

THE EARLY DAYS

DR. JOHN WALL

The most influential character in the story of the founding of the Infirmary is certainly, in my opinion, Dr. John Wall. The local historian of his time – Nash, in his *History of Worcestershire,* wrote:

DR JOHN WALL 1708-

> *"This learned Physician was a native of the County of Worcester, born at Powick in 1708 the only son of John Wall, an opulent tradesman, who served as Mayor in 1703."*

John Wall junior, after studying Classics, Mathematics, Algebra, Philosophy and Literary pursuits at Merton College, Oxford, studied Medicine at St. Thomas Hospital, taking his degree of Bachelor of Physic in 1736.

Dr. Wall set up practice in White Ladies Close in Worcester. Because of his wide medical knowledge and his charismatic personality, he soon became well known. In 1740 he married Catherine, the youngest daughter of Martin Sandys Esquire, uncle of the First Lord Sandys of Ombersley. He built a Palladian Mansion in Foregate Street, from where he ran his medical practice.

Dr.Wall's practice was incredibly vast by today's standards. He consulted as far away as Stratford–on–Avon, Kidderminster and

Ludlow. Visits were sometimes lengthy affairs lasting several days. Nash remarks that *"his practice as a Physician was particularly distinguished by benevolence, courtesy, penetration and success, but his benevolence displayed itself in its utmost extent in his unremitting attention to the poor."* Three quarters of Worcester's population were said to be his patients.

So when the newly appointed Bishop - Isaac Maddox - came to Worcester in 1743, he found Dr. John Wall eager to join his campaign for the foundation of a charitable infirmary, designed to relieve the physical sufferings of the poor, and the search for medical knowledge.

Bishop Maddox was an ardent advocate of social reforms and he set about raising money from Sermons and Lectures. Subscriptions and donations poured in from the local landed gentry – Sir John Rushout, The Earl of Coventry, Lord Northwick, Lord Lyttleton, and Lord Berkeley – to name but a few!

An old house in Silver Street was purchased in 1745 for £100. After considerable renovation, the doors opened in 1746 becoming only the seventh infirmary outside London.

The four physicians – Dr John Wall, Dr. Thomas Attwood, Dr. James MacKenzie and Dr. Thomas Cameron- appointed the first members of staff:

Thomas Bourne	Apothecary	£15. 0s. 0d per annum.
John King	Secretary	£10. 10s. 0d. per annum
Mrs White	Matron	£6. 0s. 0d. per annum.
Nurse Goslin		£3. 10s. 0d. per annum.
Patience Perry	Maidservant	£3. 0s. 0d. per annum.

Although the Infirmary opened on January 11th, there were no beds purchased until June -five beds for the patients and one bed for the staff.! Towards the end of the first year a box of 'Surgeons

Instruments' was purchased, together with a 'sweating box'. A Christmas box of *5/-* was awarded to the nurse for good behaviour! Nurses were regarded as domestic servants.

During the first three years there had been 960 admissions. Among the cured were dropsies, mortifications, scrophulus, scarbuttick and fistulous ulcers, empyema, inflammation of the eyes, simple and compound fractures, St. Vitus Dance, rheumatism, cancers, cataracts, epilepsy, a gun shot through the liver, five amputations and one boy 'cut for stone'.

Only patients with letters of recommendation from subscribers were admitted. The 'rules' of the hospital were read out to them every week. (No one with an infectious disease was allowed in, or expectant mothers, the dying or of unsound mind.) Smoking, swearing, card playing and dice were all forbidden. A cook and a Chaplain were engaged in 1749, then in 1750 a porter to evict trouble-makers.

By 1751 Worcester Infirmary had become famous, mostly for Dr. Wall's treatment of sore throats in scarlet fever and diphtheria. He was a prolific medical writer, and the first to recognise *angina pectoris* as a symptom of heart disease. His son, Dr. Martin Wall, Emeritus Professor of Surgery at Merton College, Oxford, collected all of his writings into one volume and published them in 1780.

Malvern Water captivated his interest and by 1756 he had discovered its extreme purity. Dr. John Wall's paper, *Observations and Experiments of Malvern Water*, was re-published many times, together with 79 case-histories of water-cures. The wits of the 18th Century wrote: "The Malvern Water", said Dr. John Wall "Is famous for containing just nothing at all".

In addition to his many interests and activities, in June 1751 he and his friend William Davis – apothecary of Broad Street – set up the first "Porcelain Manufactory", under the name "Worcester Tonquin Manufacturers" in imitation of the Chinese fashion.

A large manor house on Warmstry Quay had been converted into a factory producing porcelain. Dr. Wall remained its consistent and respected head for 25 years. In fact, the years 1751 – 1776 are justifiably called the Dr. Wall period. Most of the porcelain made at Worcester under Dr. Wall was Chinese in style, and was carefully and beautifully hand-painted. These pieces are now much sought after. The 'Porcelain Manufactory' did not acquire its royal warrant until the visit of George III in 1788.

Dr. Wall was Treasurer of the Worcester Infirmary and the Three Choirs Festival. He was an accomplished artist and scientist – so a man of many talents.

Worcester is indeed indebted to Dr.Wall for bringing prosperity and good health care to its citizens.

THE ARTICHOKE FIELD

In the Silver Street hospital report for 1765 the governors found it necessary to consider purchasing or erecting a more convenient building for the accommodation of the sick - the existing one being "in a ruinous condition and necessarily requiring constant repair at a considerable annual expense".

Consequently, in July of that year, it is minuted that the Governors of the Infirmary "ordered that the proposals this day delivered in by Mr Joseph Millington for the sale of two acres of land situate in the Artichoke Field for building a proper house upon for the use of the Infirmary be accepted at the purchase money of £200".

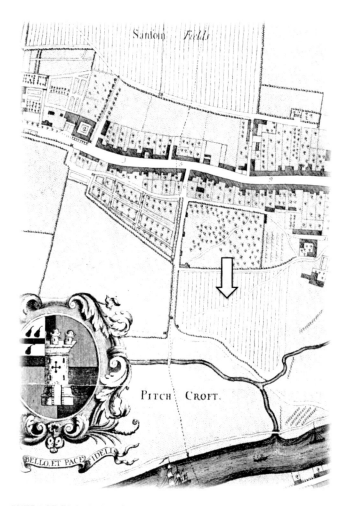

EXTRACT FROM THE 1740 PLAN OF WORCESTER: THE ARROW
SHOWS THE LOCATION OF THE ARTICHOKE FIELD

Edward Garlick magnanimously supplied the £200 required for the
purchase of the land. He was experienced in hospital planning and
advised on many aspects, including "keeping the washery away
from the building because of the noisesome steams and effluvias".

They were to have "private necessaries" (water-closets) convenient to the wards with a constant supply of water.

When the building on the Artichoke Field began in March 1767 the governors saw to it that all of Mr Garlick's advice was followed. Anthony Keck had been appointed architect, at a fee of £250. Mr Keck was a local man and friend of Dr. Wall who also designed St. Martin's Church in the Cornmarket, and Highgrove, now the home of the Prince of Wales.

In the spring of 1768 the building site was a scene of activity. Dr. Wall, now in his sixty-first year, looked over from the back of his house in Foregate Street. He must have watched the progress of the building with more than ordinary satisfaction – a tribute to the rising prosperity of his native city and due in no small measure to his own foresight and industry in establishing the Worcester Porcelain factory. He would often walk onto the site as his garden adjoined the property, being separated from it by Dr. Wall's Walk – now known as Infirmary Walk. The Doctor had good reason to be very proud of the great enterprise.

The brickworks were on Pitchcroft providing bricks just for the building of the hospital. The stone was supplied by "Samuel Ward of Bath".

On Michaelmas Day in 1770 there stood on the Artichoke Field, overlooking Pitchcroft, a handsome new infirmary. The proud citizens of Worcester admired its Georgian grandeur. The historian, Nash said "I have the satisfaction to think that all was well done: that the house is large, commodious and perfectly strong: that the whole of the plan was executed with great frugality and economy, and it is hoped would continue for ages, an honour to the County and a comfortable asylum to many sick and lame".

The building had cost £6,085 9s 9p. The patients and equipment were transferred to the new premises in September 1771.

The present entrance hall was used as 'Out Patients', and what is now the Board Room was the Physician's Room. The area latterly used as 'Out Patients' was a wash-house and coal-yard. 'Wheeley Lea' – was the men's ward and 'Rushout' the women's ward. Each ward accommodated 20 beds.

On the north side of the Physician's room was the Matron's Office, and opposite was the Apothecary's room. On the south side was the Surgeon's room (latterly the corridor leading up to X-Ray and Bates Wards). Upstairs, above the Physician's room was the Chapel. What was latterly Ganderton Ward comprised two small wards, and what became Garlic Ward were staff bedrooms. The top floor was added later.

Throughout 1773 there were 445 in-patients and 522 out-patients. Of the 445 in-patients 217 were 'cured,' 25 'relieved', 4 discharged themselves, 2 were incurable, 3 were discharged for misbehaviour, and 24 had died (maybe the others never got better!).

Sadly, in 1776 Dr. John Wall died and was replaced by Dr. James Johnson. The nurses were petitioning for extra help and pay, and the number of beds was reduced to 30 through lack of funds (sounds familiar!).

In 1781 sixpence a day was put aside to provide three nurses with a pint of ale, although it seems the Matron had to pay for her own. Several bequests to the Infirmary that year enabled them to increase the number of beds to 58. In 1790 Matron was put in charge of the wine and brandy and, by 1792, the beds increased to 65 and ladies were invited, for the first time, to become subscribers. Carriages travelling in Dr.Wall's Walk had caused several accidents, so bollards had to be placed at either end – they are still there today.

So, by the end of the 18th Century with the Infirmary well-established, Dr. Wall had seen his dream come true. He had been such a great inspiration to all who worked with him, and was held in great esteem and affection.   It was said of him (Nash of Worcestershire):

"In all concerns of life and particularly in his practice, he was distinguished by an uncommon sweetness and cheerfulness of disposition: which in union with his extensive knowledge, and penetrating discernment, attracted the affection and secured the confidence of those who required his professional assistance. To his zeal and diligence the City and County of Worcester are in no small degree indebted for the advantage of their Infirmary. His zeal was increased by its establishment, and was still further animated by its success. He gave it constant and regular attendance during his whole life, under very trying circumstances of fatigue and indisposition. The Governors of the Infirmary have recorded, in terms of great respect, their sense of the obligations they owe to his assiduity. After a life devoted to Worcestershire and its people."

After a lingering illness, Dr. John Wall died on June 27th 1776, in Bath, aged 67 years. He is buried in the Abbey Church.

"After a life of labour, for the good of others" From HIS TOMBSTONE

"Nature gave him talents; a benevolent heart, directed the application of them to the study and practice of a profession most beneficial to mankind."

CASTLE STREET

THE COUNTY GAOL IN CASTLE STREET CIRCA 1920

The new Infirmary stood in Salt Lane which ran down the north side of the Artichoke Field. Salt Lane was so named because, probably since Roman times, cartloads of salt had regularly been brought down from Droitwich using this lane to reach the inland port at South Quay, on the River Severn, for distribution around the world.

In 1813 Parliament decreed that Worcester should build a secure prison. The County Gaol was built opposite the infirmary in the style of a medieval castle, so the name of the street was changed to 'Castle Street'.

The gaol was an all-male general prison holding all categories of prisoners from murderers to political prisoners. For the very young the gaol had its own school-master who lived at No.1 Easy Row.

Public hangings and whippings were held until 1863. Great crowds gathered to watch the spectacle which took place on top of the Gate House Tower. After displaying the bodies, they were taken along a secret tunnel into the infirmary where they were dissected by the surgeons. Plaster casts of the murderers' heads were taken, to study the 'scalp bumps'. It was believed that one could tell a person's character by reading their 'bumps'. The 'Death Masks' are now on display at the George Marshall Medical Museum in Worcester.

After 1863 all executions were held within the gaol, the last one taking place in 1919 was of a Chinaman convicted of murdering a fellow Chinaman in Warley Woods. The gaol finally closed down soon after this.

SOME OF THE DEATH MASKS IN THE GEORGE MARSHALL MEDICAL MUSEUM

DR. WALL'S HOUSE IN FOREGATE STREET

43 FOREGATE STREET AS IT LOOKED IN 1922

Returning to Worcester in 1739 to set up his medical practice, Dr Wall first lived in White Ladies Close off the Tything. The following year he married Catherine Sandys, niece of his guardian Lord Sandys, and purchased the Green Dragon Inn at 43, Foregate Street. Chambers History of Worcester (1801) – states:

> *"The Inn stood back from the road which ran through what was then a suburb outside the ancient walls of the City. Dr Wall bought the property and built in front of the old buildings, and level with the street, a house admirable in its design and bearing, proof in its structure and arrangement that it was the work of an artist".*

The original inn building was used as Dr Wall's art studio, where he painted mainly classical subjects with a medical theme. Some of these paintings are on display at the Worcester Porcelain Museum.

The method of extending a building forward was, I believe, used again in 1745 when the Silver Street hospital was purchased and extended, and Dr Wall was appointed Treasurer. When it became necessary to replace this hospital, Dr Wall would have been deeply involved with the planning and building of the new hospital in Castle Street, and would often walk across from his house nearby to check on the progress of the builders.

Dr Wall died in 1776 followed by his widow in 1796. 43 Foregate Street was then successively in the occupancy of Peter Suard and Lady Grasley. In 1808 the house was bought by Dr George Woodyatt of the Worcester Infirmary for £2,000. Dr Charles Hastings married the eldest of Dr. Woodyatt's eight daughters, Hannah, in 1823. The following year Dr Hastings moved into the house, where he carried on his medical practice, but he never actually owned it - Dr George Woodyatt (who died in 1824) had left the house in his will to Eliza Wall, a relative of Dr John Wall.

While still in the occupation of Dr Hastings, Eliza Wall sold this grand house, to John Hughes in 1858. Following the death of Sir Charles Hastings in 1866, his son George Woodyatt Hastings continued to live in the house until he retired to Malvern, to live in Barnard's Green House.

There are now two blue plaques erected on the front of 43 Foregate Street, in recognition of the links to Dr John Wall and to Sir Charles Hastings. The house is now converted into offices, an Italian restaurant and a bar.

VICTORIANS

SIR CHARLES HASTINGS: 1794 – 1886

SIR CHARLES HASTINGS (1794-1886)

It is well known that Sir Charles Hastings founded the British Medical Association (BMA) here in Worcester, but what else made him such a revered and popular figure in the 19th Century?

Charles was the son of the Rector of Martley, a village just outside Worcester. As a boy, he showed remarkable attention to any creature that was sick or ailing and expressed a desire to enter the medical profession. In 1810 he was apprenticed to a Stourport apothecary and then attended a school of anatomy in London. At the age of 18, though possessing no formal medical qualifications and against strong opposition – including from a member of the Royal College of Surgeons – he was elected by the Governors, as House Surgeon to the Worcester Infirmary. He virtually took over the running of the hospital, and the clinical and management standards were vastly improved.

In 1815 Charles went to Edinburgh to study for three years for his medical degree, where he was the first student to use a microscope for his studies. Returning to Worcester he took the more prestigious post of Junior Physician.

Early in his career, Charles Hastings became convinced that the health of the public should be the responsibility of the state. With his experience of the occupational diseases of the local porcelain workers and glovers of the city, he knew it was not enough for a doctor to be concerned only with the cure of disease, it was his duty to prevent it. Only a professional body organised nationally could do this, so he organised a meeting of like-minded medical men who were keen to follow his ideas, and in 1832 set up the Provincial Medical and Surgical Society, which in 1856 became the British Medical Association (BMA).

On the site currently occupied by the Odeon Cinema, the Worcester Public Library & Hastings Museum stood. It opened in 1836, with great ceremony. Hastings presented his own valuable specimens to the natural history collection. But the episode for which Charles Hastings is most remembered, locally, is the cholera epidemic of 1832 which claimed many lives and caused widespread panic.

Cholera first hit Worcester in a crowded area of abject poverty known as 'the pinch' off Hylton Road, when a rag collector became ill and died within 16 hours. In the summer heat the disease rapidly spread and reached epidemic proportions. In the ensuing hysteria many local churchmen put the cholera visitation down to evil living, and sadly the local paper echoed this. Many people left the city's squalid teeming tenements to set up home on Ronkswood Hill, Elbury Mount and Rainbow Hill – which were then mostly green and undeveloped.

Rising above the tide of prejudice and superstition to minister to the sick with great courage and devotion, Charles Hastings tackled the problem head-on. By his self-sacrifice and fearless courage, when others fled, he saved the population.

Charles personally attended every case of cholera, and saw to the speedy burial of the dead, and to the cleansing of insanitary places. The plague was stayed. A special hospital was set up on Henwick Hill, while a place of refuge was opened near Bath Road. A mass grave for the dead was dug at Tallow Hill, opposite the former Beehive Inn, and scores of citizens were buried before the epidemic was halted. It was not until another outbreak, later in the century, that it was proved conclusively that cholera was spread by contaminated water.

At that time, there was no proper water supply in the city and few sanitary arrangements. Where they did exist, privies and cesspools were crowded against the houses, and shared by a dozen or so families. Slaughter-houses and tanneries disposed of their waste into the gutters.

Reports by the Worcester Board of Health in 1832 and 1849 condemned the filthy conditions and recommended a new complete system of sewers. Eventually, in 1858 a water-works supplied clean drinking water to the city. Charles Hastings was at the forefront of pressing for these improvements, and also the building of 'model-dwellings' in 1854 – the fore-runner of later 'council houses'.

In the following ten years the death rate was halved. Hastings was knighted in 1850 and he retired from the staff of the Worcester Infirmary in 1863. He was the first in Britain to use a microscope for medical research and a pioneer in the use of the stethoscope.

He died in 1866, aged 72, at Barnard's Green House in Malvern, where he had lived since his retirement, and was buried at Astwood Cemetery in Worcester. A window was created in his honour in Worcester Cathedral in 1932 – a century after the foundation of the BMA.

THE JENNY LIND CHAPEL

Prior to the appointment of the first Chaplain, William Griffin, in 1764, the local clergy took it in turns to conduct services and give religious instruction to the patients of Worcester Infirmary, in Silver Street. It was thought "a contented mind aided a patient's recovery".

It was customary in the mid-eighteenth century to regard disease as a punishment for bad living, or the result of a miasma or evil vapour from swamps and sewers. Thus, the Reverend Sir James

JENNY LIND

Stonehouse MD advised patients "to make use of their vacant days and sleepless nights", "they should examine their hearts, the more able should help to attend the less fortunate and in the event of no relief being obtained, they should not suspect the skill and integrity of the medical attendants".

He also told patients "should there be a corpse lying in the next bed, they should take the opportunity of looking on the awful sight and think what is to become of the soul, and do not stay in bed too long in the mornings". "For the pillow is a treacherous councillor, and time is too precious to be lost in an unnecessary indulgence, which may be more sinful than the generality of us are aware". He was of the opinion that sin had turned the world into one great infirmary.

When the new Infirmary was built in 1771 in Castle Street, the room over the Board Room, later used as an operating theatre and sometimes ENT ward, was shared with the Chaplains as a Chapel. We can only imagine the conflict and inconvenience this caused to everyone. When William Hill became Chaplain in 1839 he pleaded for a chapel, but he had to wait several years for his wish to be granted.

In 1845 Dr. Henry Pepys, Bishop of Worcester, invited Jenny Lind to sing at the 'Three Choirs Festival' in aid of the "Society for the Relief of Widows & Orphans of the Clergy". Unfortunately she was unable to accept, but she sent a £50 donation and an offer to sing for any charity in the diocese in need of help, another year.

Now Jenny Lind was at that time only 29, and the greatest coloratura opera singer, at the height of her fame and popularity. She had triumphed in her native Sweden, in France, Germany and Austria, and during her two years in England had won the hearts and admiration of all. Her generosity and good nature were boundless, having raised money for many hospitals. Slender, graceful and fair, with a profusion of auburn curls, a fresh complexion and beautiful eyes, she was known affectionately as "The Swedish Nightingale".

The Worcester Committee decided that the Infirmary stood most in need of funds, and accordingly, a concert was arranged at College Hall (King's School) for 2nd February 1849, at which Jenny Lind would sing. The proceeds of the concert were £840, and Jenny Lind refused to accept any fee or gift. This was rather unfortunate since the Royal Porcelain Company had produced a wonderful gilded set of Honeycomb Oriental Ware specially for the "Swedish Nightingale". It is not known what happened to these items

Jenny Lind settled down in Malvern, where she lived to the end of her life.

GIFTS MADE BY WORCESTER PORCELAIN

Adjacent to the Board Room, the Chapel was built by a local firm, Messrs Joseph Wood, and cost altogether £1,138 including donations. The Architect had been instructed that the Chapel should:

- Accommodate 120 people.
- Be of easy approach for patients.
- Be readily warmed in winter.
- Be an ecclesiastical edifice.

The first service was held in the Chapel in October 1851 and the sermon preached by the Dean, Dr. John Peel. The Chaplain presented a handsome crimson altar cloth, and the SPCK gave bibles, prayer and communion books, together with 66 small prayer books. The Matron, Mrs Lovell, presented a carpet for the communion rail.

The Chapel was a great success. However, two years later the chaplain observed, among many of the inmates, a total indifference to religious exercises. His congregation's inattention however was excused in part on account of the defective state of the heating system.

At Christmas 1855 Holy Communion was held for the first time, after the purchase of a chalice, a flagon, a patten and alms dish.

In 1865 a good attendance at the chapel was attributed to the good example of the excellent Matron Lovell. One January day for instance no less than 54 people were present at the service. Also, in 1865 the Citizens of Worcester presented a handsome harmonium and a Mr Cox was appointed as organist. Three years later, lighting and some ornamentation were added.

Mr William Elgar – piano tuner, and father of our own Sir Edward Elgar - was called in to repair the Harmonium in 1872. In 1873 Gerald Crecy Parnell, a house-surgeon, took over as organist and

THE JENNY LIND CHAPEL

21

was thought to "render the services brighter and more cheerful by playing the harmonium". In 1961 Miss Britain, a Nursing Tutor, designed and worked a fine linen Altar Cloth which she donated to the Chapel and the 'Friends of the Hospital' gave an altar book and sanctuary lamp, suspended by chains.

In addition to services for patients, many staff members have taken the opportunity to have their own marriages and christenings celebrated at the Jenny Lind Chapel. The very last person to be christened here was William Young, baby son of Tim and Karen Young, who was christened by Hospital Chaplain Jackie Hughes in 1997. Karen Young is Matron of Pershore Cottage Hospital.

A memorial stained-glass window commemorating 240 years of Nursing at the Royal Infirmary was installed on the south side of the chapel in 2011. Although the building is no longer used as a chapel, it is a listed building – so is being cared for and restored to its original state.

THE NAMING OF THE WARDS

The wards were not immediately given names but referred to by their location in the building, such as 'North first floor', 'South ground floor ', for example. Not until later in the nineteenth century were names given to the wards, and the names used were usually to honour people who had made large donations of money, with the only exception being the Bates Wards.

The donors were big-hearted and generous men, part of the culture of benevolence found in the days before the National Health Service (NHS). They had a strong sense of duty and felt they needed to set an example to others in their generosity. The following pages give a brief account of the lives of these benevolent men.

RUSHOUT WARD

- Male medical patients
- Ground Floor – North

SIR JOHN RUSHOUT (4th Baronet) was born in 1685, the 4th son of Sir James Rushout. Sir John was educated at Eton and in 1713 he was elected Member of Parliament for Malmsbury and then Evesham in 1722. He married Anne Compton daughter of the Earl of Northampton in 1729. He was Treasurer of the Navy 1743 – 1744 when he

PORTRAIT OF THE RT HON SIR JOHN RUSHOUT 4TH BT. 1685 – 1775. BY SIR GODFREY KNELLER BT. (1716)

became a privy councillor. In 1762 he became Father of the House until he retired in 1768.

He was said to be an interesting personality and a noted philanthropist. He was one of the very early subscribers to the hospital. Sir John presented the infirmary with his bust, which is now at the Charles Hastings Education Centre. He gave £500 towards the new building in Castle Street and his son was also a generous contributor.

Sir John Rushout died in 1775, still showing cheerfulness and politeness to his visitors.

MADDOX WARD
- Female medical patients
- Top Floor North

ISAAC MADDOX was born in 1697 in Aldersgate, London, where his father was a stationer. He lost both parents while he was young and was sent to be apprenticed to a pastry cook, but he was too fond of 'book reading'. He quickly realized he was cut out for better things.

So in 1718 he won a scholarship to Edinburgh University to study theology. In 1723 he was ordained deacon in London and following several ecclesiastic posts around the country, not staying long in any post, he became Bishop of St. Asaph in 1736. In 1745 he came to Worcester. Horace Walpole wrote, sarcastically, "*Maddox of St. Asaph has wriggled himself into the See of Worcester*". He stayed in Worcester until his death in 1759.

He was a lover of family life and had three children. Though of an amiable and benevolent disposition it was said, '*he had the air and mien of a butcher rather than a Bishop*' and also, '*seldom have the solemn functions of an English Bishop been discharged with more private dignity and public advantage than in the instance of Dr. Maddox*'.

He used his power for good and not for his own ends. The legacy he left in the form of Worcester Infirmary lives on. His strenuous efforts to promote a hospital for the city were a great advantage to it and its citizens.

GANDERTON WARD
- Female orthopaedic patients
- 1st Floor South

CHARLES GANDERTON was a bachelor living at No. 29 Bridge Street, Pershore in 1886. He was a member of a successful wool stapling family. Quiet and retiring by nature he was a small, dapper man dressed usually in black, with a stock round his neck. He was a great philanthropist, donating money to many local good causes. In 1886 he had anonymously given £5,000 to the infirmary for improving facilities for nurses and maids living in.

Altogether, Charles Ganderton gave and bequeathed £21,109 to the hospital, including bequests of £7,000 when he died in 1893, together with the residue of his estate.

GARLICK WARD
- Male surgical patients
- 1st Floor North

EDWARD GARLICK was one of the infirmary's principal benefactors. He was an eminent sugar baker of Bristol, a Justice of the Peace for the County of Gloucester. It was said of him, *'to the calls of real distress his compassionate mind was ever attentive'*.

After giving £200 for the purchase of the Artichoke Field, the hospital governors hoped that Mr Garlick would communicate such advice and directions with regard to the building, besides the conduct of the house, as his great humanity and experience qualified him to give. He must have been gratified to realize that they did indeed follow his advice, and for the grand opening of the Hospital in 1771 he travelled up from Bristol. He died in August 1781.

BONAKER WARD
- Male orthopaedic patients
- Top Floor South

Very little is known about the REVEREND WILLIAM BALDWIN BONAKER who was born in 1782 and served as a minister in Honeybourne, near Worcester. However, in 1850 he was presented to the Bishop of Worcester for being continually absent from his parish.

He lived at Prussia House in Evesham, and when he died in 1881, he left a major legacy of £8,762 to the infirmary. The money was intended for the building of a new ward, to be named after him. The Bonaker ward for children was formally opened on the 18th January 1886 by the Countess Beauchamp. It later became the male orthopaedic ward.

WHEELEY LEA WARD

- Female surgical patients
- Ground Floor South

JOHN WHEELEY LEA was born & baptised in May 1791 at Feckenham in Worcestershire, one of the seven children of Thomas and Susanna Lea, who were Yeoman Farmers. 'Wheeley', John's middle name, was probably his mother's maiden name. It was quite common for children to be given their mother's maiden as a middle name.

JOHN WHEELEY LEA, MAYOR OF WORCESTER (1849–1850) BY UNKNOWN ARTIST; COLLECTION: WORCESTER CITY MUSEUMS

John trained as an apothecary and druggist at No.68 Broad Street, Worcester. He was married to Elizabeth Mason of Leominster in 1817, they had three children. Six years later John became sole proprietor of the shop and advertised for a partner. A certain

William Perrins was the successful applicant and so the famous Lea & Perrins partnership was formed in 1823.

After the tragic death of his wife and son in 1833, Wheeley Lea involved himself in developing and expanding the famous Worcestershire Sauce which was created after a recipe was presented to the partners by a nobleman returning from Bengal, so the story goes. However, no one knows the true story. The exotic sauce became hugely successful around the world, making the partners very wealthy indeed.

John Wheeley Lea generously made many donations to the infirmary. In 1840 he was appointed Inspector of Drug, the same year he moved into a grand house in Lansdowne Crescent, next door to his partner and friend – William Perrins.

John Wheeley Lea was intensely involved in local politics and had served as an Alderman, and was elected Mayor of Worcester in 1835, and again in 1849. In 1864 he financed the building of the almshouses in Infirmary Walk and had the school house rebuilt next to them. That year a gift of £500 to the hospital from himself and William Perrins was one of many he gave.

John Wheeley Lea died of acute dyspepsia in March 1874 in his 83rd year at Stansford House, Upper Wick. His son, Charles Wheeley Lea, born in 1827, became a partner in the sauce business in 1857. Charles, like his father, gave generously to the Worcester infirmary. In 1895 he donated £1,000, and in his will bequeathed it £10,000. He also left £2,000 to the dispensary and £1,000 to opthalmics. In recognition of his generosity the Infirmary named the South Ward after him. His widow Amy donated money for Southbank Hospital after he died in 1898.

BATES MEDICAL & SURGICAL WARDS

- For children
- In 1950's Extension (now demolished)

TOM BATES the elder was appointed general surgeon in 1879 and served for 31 years. He was instrumental in setting up the X-Ray department in the basement. He also requested an electric light in the Operating Room (subsequently ENT ward). He resigned in October 1904. Tom Bates the younger, his son, took over.

TOM BATES (SENIOR)

Tom Bates the elder wrote to the committee:

"If you should give me the privilege of attending, as a mere spectator, the practice of the Infirmary, your kindness would lessen the grief I feel at the official severance from my colleagues and from a charity whose goodness and welfare lie near to my heart, and within whose walls I have spent some of the happiest and some of the most anxious hours of my life".

He was devoted to the infirmary! Who could deny such a request? So he never really retired – he just stayed on. When his sons went to war in 1914 he volunteered to work full time.

His skill as a surgeon was quite remarkable, and he was a good teacher. He also was a cultured man with a liking for art and politics, fond of cricket and billiards. He spoke French and had a great sense of humour. In the darkest days of the war Bates contracted

Influenza but for three days remained at work, in spite of a fever and blizzard-like weather. After a week he died in April 1916.

Many nurses believed that the restless ghost, which allegedly haunted the children's wards at night, was Tom Bates – he was so reluctant to leave the building.

THE PRIVATE WARDS

The private individual rooms (always known as P.W.) were on the top floor, on the corridor between Maddox and Bonaker wards. There were approximately 10 rooms, usually occupied by private patients but staffed by regular hospital staff. Sometimes if a nurse became ill, she would be nursed on P.W. and if she required surgery then Matron would accompany her to theatre.

EARS NOSE & THROAT WARD

This ward (always known as ENT) was on the floor below P.W. on the corridor between Ganderton and Garlick Wards. This ward had previously been used as the Operating Theatre prior to 1932 and up until 1851 it had also served as the Chapel.

There was a large room containing 10 - 12 beds for children usually in for Tonsillectomy and Adenoidectomy - a very common procedure in the 1950's & 1960's. You had to be extra careful to watch red-heads as they were known to 'bleed' more severely than other people. Several smaller rooms were for adults undergoing ear operations such as mastoid, or nasal operations.

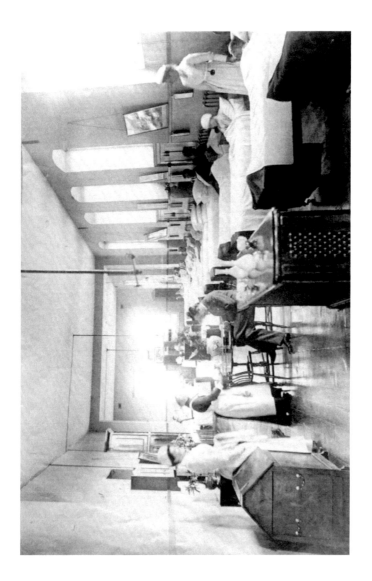

BONAKER WARD CIRCA 1900

BONAKER WARD C1900

THE HOUSE OF INDUSTRY, TALLOW HILL

By Muriel Clayson, Clinical Nurse Tutor.

In 1794, 23 years after the Worcester Infirmary had moved from Silver Street to Castle Street, the House of Industry was opened, on the summit of Tallow Hill, in what was described as *'a park-like meadow overlooking the Malvern Hills'*.

At the time, the poor were the responsibility of the Parish, granted 'outdoor relief' with suitable work found for them wherever possible. It was intended that the House of Industry was run as a home and occupational centre for the unemployed poor. The children were apprenticed to local industries, such as the makers of coarse woollen cloth, gloves, for example.

By the time of the Poor Law Report in 1834 this relatively philanthropic attitude had changed. Outdoor relief was no longer allowed and the poor could only receive benefits in a work-house. So the House of Industry became the Worcester Union Workhouse, run by a board of 22 male Guardians, with a reputation for harsh conditions. Admission was greatly feared by the unfortunate poor. Considerable rebuilding in Victorian times enlarged it into a complex of 10 blocks, with a laundry and mortuary. It was now named 'Hillborough'.

From a time capsule discovered during demolition in 1987, we learned that the residents of 1894 comprised 40 able-bodied men, 66 able-bodied women, 74 old men, 8 male imbeciles, 4 couples and 20 infants. Conditions were still oppressive, although in 1894 women were also elected to the Board of Guardians which improved the lot of the residents. For example, milk was provided for all, not just the under 5 year-olds. Improved clothing, leisure facilities and education of the children slowly came into being, but the spectre of the workhouse remained very real.

During World War II residents were moved to Evesham, when Hillborough became the Headquarters of RAF Fighter Command. After their return in 1946 Hillborough was described as a Public Assistance Institution of 325 beds, including an infirmary of 24 beds. Following re-organisation, with the advent of the NHS in 1948, the complex comprised:

- Shrub Hill Hospital – with four wards for sick and elderly patients;
- Shrub Hill Maternity Unit – of 18 beds; and
- Hillborough Welfare Residential Home – as Part 3 Accommodation.

In 1969 sweeping changes began as a Government initiative. *"The Victorian complex of buildings will have to be closed down"* (local newspaper 1969). Gradually, transfers were made. In 1979 the sick, elderly patients moved to a purpose-built unit on the new District General Site in Newtown Road – as the Newtown Branch of the Worcester Royal Infirmary.

By 1986, demolition of the buildings began and the site was sold to Westbury Homes. The Nurses Home was converted into flats for single persons. The Board Room and Dining Room was sold to Worcester Muslim association. The former is now a Mosque. Significantly, in 1988 the St. Paul's Hostel for the homeless transferred to the site, a modest return of the original hopes for the House of Industry.

THE LIFE & TIMES OF DR. JAMES GULLY, 1808 - 1883

Although never involved in the Worcester Infirmary itself, he was such a remarkable character who nevertheless had great influence over the health and prosperity of the County of Worcestershire – a man larger than life – yet short and insignificant in appearance.

It was Dr. James Gully who, nearly a century after Dr. Wall's discoveries brought the rich and famous flocking to Malvern for the 'Water Cure' when he established, with his partner Dr. James Wilson, the foremost centre for hydrotherapy in England.

James Manby Gully was born in 1808 in Jamaica, son of a wealthy plantation owner and 8th child in a family of 13 children. The infant mortality rate was very high in Jamaica, so James was sent to Liverpool to be educated and became a school friend of William Ewart Gladstone – the later Prime Minister. Aged 15 he was apprenticed to an Apothecary & Surgeon, and later studied medicine in Edinburgh, where he knew Charles Darwin. He was said to be 'a born Doctor'. He also studied under 'Dupuytren'(a well-known surgeon) in Paris.

In 1829 the Gully family lost its fortune with the abolition of slavery and personal tragedy struck repeatedly. He was heart-broken when his fiancée died, then later his first wife perished of small-pox, after bearing him four children. Fanny, the youngest died of croup in 1840. Dr. Gully watched helplessly as orthodox treatments not only failed, but caused great suffering. Dr. Gully was keen to try alternative treatments, even including clairvoyance, and being appalled by the dangers of conventional drugs he was readily converted to hydrotherapy when his friend Dr. James Wilson related his experiences of new treatments at Graefenburg Spa in Austria.

His second marriage in 1840 was to a wealthy widow 17 years his senior, but she was very domineering and would not allow his children to live with them. So they split up two or three years after the wedding.

Dr. Gully had already an established practice in London, where he was consulted by many famous people, including the Prime Minister, Lord Aberdeen, and such was the power of his personality, that his fame spread throughout Europe. He had a natural literary gift and wrote many books and articles on medical subjects. However, he was willing to leave all this behind him – and set up a new "Graefenburg" with the revolutionary 'water-cures'. Searching for a similar location in England they found Malvern to be perfect in every way.

So in 1842 Doctors Wilson & Gully arrived in Malvern, where they leased the Crown Hotel for 21 years. Dr. Gully's son, William, who was destined to become "Speaker of the House of Commons", described how they also bought two houses, next to 'Warwick House', where they set-up the accommodation for their patients. The two houses were joined by a small bridge, at first floor level, known to all as "the bridge of sighs".

The 'water cures' although quickly established amongst the rich and famous, was violently opposed by orthodox medicine, and the greatest opponent was Sir Charles Hastings of Worcester. He was very influential in the medical world, but maybe a little jealous of the lucrative new methods.

Because they *were* extremely lucrative, in fact Dr. Gully became probably the richest man in Worcestershire at that time. But Doctors Wilson & Gully maintained that their methods enabled the patient to combat illness by natural means. The basis of the treatment was that pure water, pure air, a proper diet and regular exercise are the great agents in effecting the cure of disease, by aiding the natural efforts of the body, through the instrumentality of the nervous system. So patients coming to stay in Malvern from disease ridden cities of Victorian England, and elsewhere, were bound to benefit. No one had yet realized that bacteria could cause disease and viruses were still unknown.

Water treatments included – baths, douches, wet wraps, cold and hot water, often very unpleasant, indeed horrific experiences, but people were willing to pay high prices for being tortured. They often endured a strict and humiliating regime, suffering extremes of temperature in the 'steam baths' and then ice cold jets of water.

The two doctors however parted company after many disagreements over treatment and in 1846 Dr. Gully was left in complete control. Dr. James Gully became more and more successful and wealthy; his patients included Alfred, Lord Tennyson, Charles Darwin & family, Charles Dickens, Thomas Carlisle and Florence Nightingale – who at first was sceptical of the 'water cure'.

Dr. Gully invested in many varied projects locally. He owned the 'Malvern News', was Chairman of the Imperial Hotel Company, a Director of the Worcester City & County Bank, and the Worcester, Oxford & Wolverhampton Railway Company. He helped to establish 'Malvern College' and was Chairman of Malvern Town Commissioners for nine years. He was also a major shareholder in the Royal Worcester Porcelain Company, in fact at one time owned over 5,000 shares at £500 a share – more than the owner.

Then in 1870 all this changed. His greatest mistake was to fall in love with Florence Ricardo, the beautiful auburn-haired wife of Captain Ricardo. Initially she consulted Dr. Gully regarding her 'depression'. Later she persuaded her alcoholic husband to seek his help. Captain Ricardo left Malvern and was found dead in Cologne, the following year. . . Florence and Dr. Gully formed a deep attachment – travelling extensively. To the great consternation of the Malvern citizens Dr. Gully suddenly resigned and left Malvern, in the New Year of 1872. He bought a house very near to Florence's home on Tooting Common. Florence had an abortion in 1873 – allegedly performed by Dr. Gully.

In 1875 their friendship ended and Florence, after a whirlwind courtship, married Charles Bravo, a young Barrister. Within five months her new husband was dead – of poisoning. His last words apparently were, "I have taken poison for Dr. Gully, don't tell Florence".

A "Trial by Inquest" was held. Dr. Gully volunteered to give evidence to help Florence, who was under suspicion of murder, but in so doing, exposed the past and brought himself only humiliation and disgrace. The poison was traced to Malvern – Clerks Chemists in Church Street - where it had been purchased by Dr. Gully's groom. So suspicion fell on Dr. Gully too. The verdict – "That some person or persons unknown did feloniously and wilfully Charles Bravo kill and murder". The Charles Bravo murder has become one of the most fascinating unsolved mysteries of the Victorian era.

Alcohol eventually killed Florence, and Dr. Gully's illustrious career ended in ignominy then oblivion. Dr. James Gully died in 1883 – a remarkable life lived by a remarkable man.

IMPROVEMENTS

THE NEW NURSES HOME

THE NEW NURSES HOME - 1932

The Hospital was expanding rapidly and the number of nurses increasing, so by 1930 Mulberry House Nurses Home, that Miss Herbert built, needed to be replaced by a much larger building. Even though money was still very short, it was decided to go ahead and the 'foundation stone' was laid on 15th June 1931 – for a fine spacious three-story building, housing sixty two nurses. Lecture rooms in the basement provided more space for the School of Nursing, together with a luggage room, hair dressers and sewing room.

The individual bedrooms had polished wooden parquet flooring, wash-hand basins, fitted wardrobes and the whole building was centrally heated – bathrooms and lavatories were situated on each floor. The ground floor had a very striking black and white tiled hall floor. Separate sitting rooms for Students and Sisters. Home Sister had her own quarters, and Matron's flat at the northern end of the building had two living rooms, a bedroom, kitchen and bathroom. The building joined the main hospital along a long corridor. The extremely high standard of the facilities were very much appreciated by the Nursing Staff.

Sadly this excellent building was vacated in 2002 and later demolished. Now the nurses have nowhere to live, although much of the nurses' home had been used as offices in recent years. Mulberry House became the Maids Home for resident domestic staff.

INFIRMARY EXTENSIONS

As the 20th Century progressed the expectations of the population was changing. For example, a rapid increase in motor traffic meant that road accident victims were occupying beds needed for fee paying patients.

Two new valuable services had been set-up. One a special out-patients clinic for Nervous and Mental Diseases, and secondly Commander Spreckley's 'Rover Scout Blood Donor Service'. Initially it numbered 15 volunteers, but during the war years this local band grew into a large brigade of donors who contributed 15,147 pints of blood to the national war effort.

Doctors were clamouring for better facilities, like laboratories, X-rays and Operating Theatres – so there was a desperate need to extend the building, at Castle Street, and provide space to house the new services required with up-to-date equipment and facilities for research. So in 1930 a scheme, costing £90,000 was set up to build the extensions, due to be completed in time for the visit of HRH the Prince of Wales in October 1932.

The adoption of a 'Contributory Scheme' for wage-earners, led to an increase in income and so enabled the budget to be balanced and stabilized.

So the Governors were encouraged to go ahead with the modernising work, long awaited. An appeal to the public went out and £62,000 was quickly raised, and the work for the extension put in hand, with the remaining funds coming in over the next few months.

The scheme included large well lighted rooms, with Terrazzo Floors and Viancola Walls, all angles rounded to make cleaning easier! Electric power and light was laid on with an abundant supply of hot and cold water. Two operating theatres, named after Tom Bates the Elder, to have air circulating systems – probably the most modern in the whole country, with all the latest equipment, including X-ray viewing screens.

The floor below accommodated the latest Pathological Laboratory, named after Joseph Banks, major donor, and a small six bedded ward. A lift connected the two floors with the ground floor where the Orthopaedic department, later named Nuffield Department, with plaster room and treatment rooms were planned. The basement would be occupied by the Mortuary, and post-mortem department, and also a Coroners Court and a retiring room for the Coroners juries.

I am pleased to report that the work was completed in time for the Prince's visit. The building of the 'Bates Wards' and new X-ray department were added at a later date.

At about this time – the early 1930's – Walnut Tree House was converted into a residence for three Medical Officers. This interesting old house was at one time the 'Town House' of the Earls of Coventry and one of its amenities was a cock-pit.

In 1934 Mr Stanley Baldwin opened a Maternity and Women's department. The bed capacity of this department was small, so only abnormal cases were admitted – most babies were born at home at this time anyway.

An unwelcome visitor this year was the Death Watch beetle which cost the Infirmary £11,000 and necessitated a broadcast appeal by Bishop Perowne, who said, "From Broadway to Bredon, to the Clent and Lickey Hills and from the Malverns to Shakespeare's Country the sick have been coming to the hospital since 1745".

For some strange reason, people started contributing 'eggs' for the patients instead of money – and the awe-inspiring figure of 31,300 eggs were given creating an acute problem in storage!.

In September 1939 three thousand square yards of 'blackout material' was purchased, and the Infirmary was then ready to play its part in the Second World War. In the winter of 1940 fire watchers on the roof of the new theatre block searched the black starry sky for enemy aircraft. Many volunteers flocked to the hospital :- Drivers, Receptionists, Makers of hot drinks, Blood donors, VAD's and members of the WVS. In addition the staff increased to cope with all the extra work.

American Army Doctors regularly joined in the clinical meetings and consultations, and new professionals, almoners, therapists, scientists etc., all multiplied in numbers, and so that the very walls of the hospital were ready to burst asunder through overcrowding Henwick House was purchased for £8,000 plus two houses in Bath Road for £8,000 to ease the problem. The use of 'Ronkswood Hospital' eventually brought relief for patients and staff alike, even though it was situated on the edge of the City – a couple of miles from the Infirmary. However, less than 15 years after the building of the Extensions the extra space they provided was proving inadequate.

H.R.H. THE PRINCE OF WALES VISIT TO WORCESTER – OCTOBER 1932

Information extracted from the "Worcester Advertiser" 28th Oct. 1932:

The sun shone brilliantly from a cloudless sky. It was a never to be forgotten occasion. From an early hour, Worcester was agog with excitement – the popular Prince was coming to Worcester for three main purposes, the opening of the new Hospital extensions, the opening of the new 'widened' River Bridge and the enlargement of Cripplegate Park.

The Faithful City's welcome to His Royal Highness, the Prince of Wales was beyond description. From an early hour many thousands of people gathered along the route to welcome the first visit of the Prince. Ablaze with flags and bunting, flowers and garlands, loyal greetings were everywhere.

Diana Ogilvy – Worcester's first Lady Mayor - had the honour of greeting the Royal Party at the Guildhall. The Prince's speech included the following, "Later on I shall be visiting an important extension of the Worcester General Infirmary, and I would like to make this announcement. I believe His Majesty the King (George V) was approached as to whether the Worcester General Infirmary might have the title "Royal" and I am told by His Majesty to announce when I came here that he is only too delighted that that should be so". (applause)

Later, at the Infirmary, a guard of honour of Nurses, patients, Scouts and Guides lined the route into the Board Room. Bishop Perowne – President of the Infirmary - read the address of welcome, prior to a tour of inspection by the Royal Party.

THE PRINCE OF WALES VIST TO OPEN THE NEW NURSES HOME AND NEW EXTENSIONS

Accepting a 'Golden Key' from the Architect, Mr A.V. Rowe, His Royal Highness unlocked the door of the Nurses Home and declared the building 'open', to the delight of Matron Perry. Gifts of cheques and purses towards the extension fund were presented to the Prince in the Recreation Room. After receiving many cheques, the Prince said, "Now I have a very important announcement to make – very important to the Infirmary. It is that Sir William Morris, who was born in this City and is an old friend of mine, has asked me to announce he wants to give £26,000". There were loud gasps of astonishment at the magnitude of the gift. Sir William Morris modestly remarked that it gave him great pleasure to help his native City. The Prince led the loud applause which followed.

The Prince unveiled the memorial stone in the extension corridor and the building was dedicated by Bishop Perowne – "To the glory of God and to alleviate the suffering of men, women and children".

The Prince left shortly afterwards amid great cheering, to make his way to the Royal Worcester Porcelain Company, which was the final visit in a full itinerary. This day will long be remembered by Worcester Citizens.

RONKSWOOD HOSPITAL

Ronkswood Hospital, on the outskirts of Worcester, was built in 1938–42 by the Emergency Medical Services for treating wounded soldiers. Convoys of injured soldiers came by train to Shrub Hill Station – straight from the battlefields of Europe. The hospital accommodated 800 patients in wards of 40 beds – the wards were in long huts with no connecting corridors. The pressure was intense and the twin operating theatres often had two operating tables in each with two teams of operating staff to meet the needs of the injured men.

Many of the casualties had limbs in plaster, the casts being labelled with the underlying injuries. The casts were removed, fractures reduced and wounds cleaned and sutured. The overflows of patients were taken to Castle Street Hospital for treatment.

SISTER COOPER OUTSIDE RONKSWOOD HOSPITAL 1957

After the war, in 1951, Ronkswood Hospital was taken over by the Ministry of Pensions, and a covered walkway linking the huts was constructed. The hospital was staffed mostly by unqualified people and used as a convalescent home at that time. The Hilda Lloyd Maternity Unit was set up in 1952 – headed by Betty Woodbury. Eventually, after major upgrading of all areas, Ronkswood was incorporated into Worcester Royal Infirmary in 1966.

Medical wards were transferred from Castle Street and a new Accident & Emergency department and coronary care unit were established during the last few years. Ronkswood Hospital finally closed in 2002 and all services were transferred to the new Worcestershire Royal Hospital.

NURSES

NURSE TRAINING IN WORCESTER

MISS HERBERT AND HER NURSES ON THE STEPS OF MULBERRY HOUSE C. 1900

For centuries most nurses in most hospitals in England were untrained drudges; incompetent and often drunken Mrs Gamps – and Worcester was no different. The Doctors did not believe it necessary to train nurses. As long as they carried out the Doctor's orders, that was all that was required of them. So the standard of Nursing was never going to improve while this attitude was rife.

Matrons were difficult to keep for long once they realized they had very little 'say' in patients' treatment. In Worcester Lucy Packwood was an exception. From 1832 – 1856, for 24 years she gave splendid service. According to the hospital committee her management was unimpeachable, and to top it all, she could carve half a dozen joints for 80 people in under half an hour, and make sure all her charges received a fair share.

Recruitment of nurses remained difficult. True the salary was paltry, but they had their beer, board and residence, and when their life's work was done they were given a few shillings a week until they entered an Almshouse.

Then the Crimean War and the advent of Florence Nightingale's methods for training Nurses revolutionised the care of the sick.

In the 1860's Florence Nightingale's influence was spreading round the country and in "A Short History of Nursing" by Stewart & Dock it states: "The specially revolutionary feature of Miss Nightingale's plans for the training of nurses was, in short, nothing else than the positive mandate that the entire control of a nursing staff, as to discipline and teaching, must be taken out of the hands of men, and lodged in those of a woman". Henry Bonham–Carter, secretary of the Nightingale Fund, strongly recommended the upgrading of Matrons, with nurses answerable only to the Matron and not Doctors.

Of course the doctors were up in arms, not wishing to relinquish any power. In Worcester in 1874 a detailed scheme for Nurses Training was set up – they were to be paid £8 for the 1st year, £12 for the 2nd year, £16 for the 3rd year and £20 for the 4th year. Bright and intelligent recruits were sought, and they had to be able to read and write.

However, things did not improve even in 1888 when Miss McClelland was appointed as Matron and she began a course of lectures and established a medical library for the nurses. Recruitment remained a serious problem.

The qualities required of young girls stated, "She must be strong in mind and body; she must be able to stick doggedly to disagreeable work, face unpleasant sights, to watch the approach of death, endure the suffering of the patients". "She also should be sober, honest, truthful, trustworthy, punctual, quiet and orderly, clean and neat, patient, cheerful and kindly". She must work 80 hours a week, wait on Sister and the Doctors and patients, sweep and dust the wards, make bandages, arrowroot and egg-flip, line splints and apply leeches. Small wonder the career appealed only to a few!

But, in 1894 Miss Mary Herbert – assistant Matron at St. Thomas's Hospital Nightingale School of Nursing - came to Worcester as the new Matron. Immediately she set about improving the lot of Nurses – she ordered that a Nurse's Home of 33 bedrooms be built, standing next to the main Hospital building on Wheeley's Gardens. This fine building – Mulberry House - cost £5,000 and the 'Foundation Stone' for the new home was laid by the Countess of Coventry on 15th February 1897. The building was declared 'open' on 16th May 1898 by Lady Mary Lygon. This event also marked the 150th Anniversary of the Hospital.

Miss Herbert was a splendid nurse, a good teacher and able administrator. Her abilities were widely known and in 1903 she was invited to sit on the Nursing Board of the India Office. She wielded great influence in the hospital and was able to raise the standard of Nurse Training considerably, so that recruits for the school were much easier to find than previously.

She was the first to realize the importance of a high standard of training, in attracting good quality recruits.

She passed on all her knowledge and nursing skills to the following generations and we all owe her a great debt for her fine example.

When interviewed in 1907 by the Nursing Mirror, she commented on Nurses' salaries at the time: - "There is no salary for the first year, but the second year it is £10 and the 3rd - £15. The Theatre Nurse receives £25 to £27 and Sister's £25 - £35 per annum." Asked about hours worked Miss Herbert replied, "From 7am until 8.15pm. Night duty – Four months at a time, during which they have no nights off, but at the end they have a day's holiday". "I do not think that nurses here find nursing trying!" she said.

Miss Herbert retired in 1919 – after the War - and the school of nursing gradually developed and enlarged. By the 1940's a block system had been introduced giving the students an opportunity to attend lectures in blocks of subjects, e.g. Surgery or Medicine, the Hospital consultants lecturing, setting and marking exams. In addition, specialist Nursing Tutors taught the theory and practice of Nursing.

The 'block' system of lectures meant Nurses did not have to work their usual shifts on the wards during the weeks 'in block'. Therefore they were able to concentrate on their studies.

Previously, studying had to be fitted in around long hours on the wards, so nurses often 'nodded off' during lectures.

Most teaching was still carried on in the wards and departments, of course, and subjects including Surgery, Gynaecology, Anatomy, Physiology, Public Health, Dietetics, Child Development, Medicine, Contagious Diseases, Orthopaedics, Human Biology, Psychology, Bacteriology etc., etc., were studied.

National & Hospital Exams had to be passed at the end of three years in order to gain State Registration and go on to become a Staff Nurse.

The School of Nursing was transferred to Ronkswood Hospital in 1963 and eventually to the University of Worcester. Nurses now take degrees in Nursing but they seem to suffer from a lack of "hands-on" experience.

We have come a long way from Mrs Gamp, but most of us believe nursing is still a very worthwhile and rewarding career - a way of life like no other.

MULBERRY HOUSE NURSES HOME

STUDENT DAYS

In the 1950's most Student Nurses started their training straight from school, aged 18. At Worcester Royal Infirmary, in 1954, girls from many different countries came to train here because the English training was believed to be the best in the world. After a 12 week Preliminary Training School (P.T.S.) to assess the suitability of each candidate, the students took exams in Anatomy, Physiology and Public Health, as well as practical tests. There were 20 students in our P.T.S.

The girls (there were no male students then) were then issued with their uniforms. This consisted of 3 grey dresses with short sleeves, 14 stiff white aprons, 5 stiff collars with studs, 5 plain white caps, 5 pairs of cuffs and 3 stiff white belts. The students wore black shoes and stockings and no make-up. The Hospital Laundry washed the uniforms.

For students, it was compulsory to live in the Nurses Home, even if your family home was local. The Nurses Home was ruled over by Home Sister, who had a couple of domestic maids to help. There were also 2 bed-makers employed whose sole duty was to make all the Nurses beds. The nurses' single rooms were quite luxurious for that era, having parquet flooring, wash-handbasins, fitted wardrobes and central heating.

The main doors of the nurses' home were locked at 10.30pm and Lights-out was at 11.00pm. Anyone staying out late without a pass had to climb in through the window of Sick-bay. Unfortunately, Matron's flat was situated across the corridor from Sick-bay, so it was a bit risky, and you would never know who was in sick-bay at the time. Quite a few people were caught.

The salary for a student Nurse at that time was £6.00 a month, which had to pay for personal toiletries, clothes, travel, holidays, etc. So we didn't have much to spend on going out, but the camaraderie and fun was something remembered for life. This engendered a great sense of loyalty to one another and to the Hospital.

Once a month, on a Saturday night, a Dance was held in the Recreation Room in the Nurses Home. This was a very popular event as we were able to meet boy-friends, and soldiers from the nearby Norton Barracks would come over. Invitations were sent from the Officers' Messes at Norton and Blackmore Camps inviting Nurses for Scottish Dancing and parties, when transport was provided. These occasions were the highlight of our social calendar. We rarely went to a Pub, as it was 'not done' for females to go on their own without a 'male'.

Then there was 'Matron's Ball', an annual dance held at the Guildhall. Matron would allow us to invite a partner, who had to be 'vetted' before being allowed to attend. But we enjoyed it all.

The 3 years training was divided into 12 week periods, to be spent in each speciality, giving the student the widest experience possible. At the end of the first year examinations had to be passed, and then the white belt was replaced with a black Petersham ribbon belt, and the student given more responsibility.

My first 'ward' was Wheeley Lea, female surgery. During my time on Wheeley Lea I was taken, together with my P.T.S. group to witness my first surgical operation, an appendicectomy performed by Chief Surgeon Mr George Marshall. After only 2 minutes I fainted clean away and never saw the operation. Little did I know then that I would end up as a Theatre Sister.

Sister D.T. Brown was in charge of Wheeley Lea, and like most Sisters she was quite strict. I found myself polishing bed-pans in the sluice and cleaning anything and everything. The Sisters were unmarried, lived in special apartments in the Nurses Home, and had very few interests outside the Hospital.

My second 'ward' was Bates Surgical Children's Ward. I loved the children, but that year there was an epidemic of polio in Worcester which was devastating. The paralysis crept up the children's limbs so rapidly and then they had to be put in an "iron lung" to enable them to breath.

Christmas on Bates Surgical was magical, we were allowed to decorate the ward and a huge amount of food of all kinds was provided, and alcohol too, much to our surprise. On Christmas Eve the nurses toured the wards singing Carols, wearing their capes –

red lining out. Then on Christmas day the children all had gifts, then Father Christmas arrived to distribute even more parcels. The Mayor and V.I.P's, including Carice Elgar, would tour the wards, and then one of the surgeons would arrive to carve the turkey for the patients. It was hoped to give the patients a happy day, even though away from their relatives. The student nurses had their Christmas dinner on Boxing Day, being waited-on by the junior Doctors.

Study was carried out during off-duty times except during the Block Period. This consisted of several weeks intensive lectures given by the Consultants. There were blocks covering each general category, Surgical Block, Medical Block etc., followed by written and 'viva' examinations. ('viva' was what we called a viva voce exam)

Night Duty was also a period of 12 weeks, spent as junior to a Staff Nurse. We had to sleep in the Night Nurses Home in Bath Road. This was a huge Victorian Villa, each room was big enough to contain 3 beds, 3 wardrobes and 3 dressing tables – and still have room to swing a cat.

We were woken with a cup of tea at 6.00pm and then taken by bus down to the Infirmary, where at 7.00pm we had breakfast, going on duty at 7.30pm. Night duty was very hard work and it was always busy, because there were usually only 3 people – a Staff Nurse, Student and an auxiliary, to do everything. The Night Sisters would visit each ward to check drugs and also supervise any crises or sort any problems.

One of the lovely parts of Night duty was to hear the dawn chorus, to see the sun-rise and the mist rise up from the River Severn on summer mornings. One of the down sides was to have to eat dinner, maybe fish and chips, when we came off duty at 7.30am. Then we were taken by bus back to the Home in Bath Road.

After three years training we had to take written and practical 'State Exams' and Hospital Exams. These were quite separate but essential if you wanted to become a 'State Registered Nurse' and become a staff nurse. The practical exams were taken at a different Hospital to our training Hospital. Our group of about 20 had to go to Gloucester Royal Infirmary, which was quite daunting. However it turned out quite well for me because I was asked numerous questions about the operating theatre, techniques, naming instruments etc., and as I was actually working in the theatre at the time, I knew all the answers.

So I passed my finals in November 1957 and was offered a position as Staff-nurse in the operating theatre at Castle Street. I was then given lilac dresses to replace the drab grey, and frilly caps to wear. I was also allowed to wear a Silver Buckle on my belt. It was a great day for all of us, as we all passed our exams that year.

The nurses I trained with have gone into many different branches of nursing, all over the country and some overseas. It was a great experience and friendships made then still thrive.

Tales of some of the great characters I came into contact with during my training are included in the following pages. They each had quite remarkable experiences.

THE AUTHOR, MIRIAM HARVEY (2ND RIGHT FRONT ROW) RECEIVING PRIZE FOR SURGICAL NURSING IN 1957

MATRON MISS HERBERT IN HER OFFICE C. 1900

MATRON MISS HERBERT WITH HER NURSES OUTSIDE THE CHAPEL C. 1910

MATRONS OF WORCESTER ROYAL INFIRMARY

1745 – MRS. MARGARET WHITE
1752 – MRS. ANNE TRISTAM
1759 – MRS. WYNN
1778 – MRS. SARAH LINTON
1798 – MRS. CHARLOTTE FORD
1812 – MRS. ELIZABETH BRACE
1815 – MRS. CATHERINE PEARKES
1823 – MRS. ELIZABETH BURROWS
1832 – MRS. LUCY PACKWOOD
1856 – MRS. SOPHIA LOVELL
1861 – MRS. JANE BIGWOOD
1866 – MRS. MARIE VOYER
1869 – MRS. MARY ANN WILLIAMS
1871 – MRS. ELIZABETH McVEY
1873 – MRS. LOUISA DAVIDSON
1882 – MRS. M. SUTCLIFFE
1883 – MRS. ANNE GWYNNE
1888 – MRS. MARY JANE
McCLELLAND
1893 – MRS. EDITH BELLARS
1894 – MISS. MARY HERBERT
1919 – MISS. M.F. WATSON
1924 – MISS. M. SAVERY
1925 – MISS. ELSIE H. PERRY
1943 – MISS.EVELYN HEALEY
1960 – MISS. MAY HULME

PORTRAIT OF MISS MARY
HERBERT (MATRON FROM
1894-1919)

Until the end of the 19th century Matrons were automatically given the title of "Mrs" whether or not they were married. It was deemed improper for an unmarried lady to appear to be living in the hospital.

THE COMING OF THE N.H.S.

Throughout its history, the fortunes of the Infirmary have waxed and waned.

During the 203 years, from the founding of the Worcester Infirmary in 1746 in Silver Street – to the setting up of the NHS in 1948, the hospital was totally dependent upon financial contributions made by the local gentry, wealthy benefactors and general well-wishers in order to keep the hospital running.

Consequently, as the needs of the population grew, the financial contributions never quite met those needs and the hospital lurched from crisis to crisis, forever wondering how they were going to cover the costs of running the hospital. Over the years many appeals were made by the Bishop and other prominent citizens, and the public were very generous in their donations. Ladies' committees ran picnics and concerts to raise funds. The Hospital Sunday Fund and the Worcester Hospital Contributors Association also raised many thousands of pounds.

But the breaking point came following the end of the Second World War, when medical advances had expanded. At last the Government realized that the state should take over the responsibility of financing and running Hospitals throughout the country – including General Practitioners, Dental Services and Ophthalmic Services.

Many people could not afford any kind of medical service, unless they worked for a paternalistic company like Cadburys or the Royal Porcelain Company who provided contributory schemes, "sick clubs", for their employees.

The GP's also faced a dilemma when deciding which of their patients "deserved" to receive expensive treatments. Parents of sick children were afraid to send for the doctor in case they couldn't afford to pay the Doctor's Bill. So there were many good reasons why the state should take over the care of patients "From the cradle to the grave", providing free medical care for everyone.

The proposal to set up the National Health Service was met with hostility by many doctors who believed their autonomy was about to be removed. The controversy was quite a serious obstacle to overcome, but eventually all agreed that the scheme would be a great benefit to everyone.

Berrow's Journal in June 1948 reported, "In future, the administration of the Infirmary will be carried out by an Area Management Committee, responsible to the Regional Board in Birmingham. Special funds will be organized to provide for additional comforts for the patients. The public will be able to contribute to these funds. .... Thus, "The Friends of Worcester Royal Infirmary" was formed, which had previously been known as the "Women's Auxiliary Association."

It is difficult to see how the Infirmary could have carried on. In common with many hospitals throughout the country it was housed in centuries old buildings, constantly in need of repair. With the coming of the NHS it was possible to expand and even replace many hospital buildings.

Medical advances meant peoples' expectations grew. Where once each patient was grateful for treatment received, soon great demands were being made on the Emergency Services and new techniques and therapies taken for granted. Great advances have been made since 1948 in medical research and each citizen has access to all these advantages, treatments of a huge variety, usually locally at Worcestershire Royal Hospital.

Some people criticize the NHS, but they forget what huge problems existed prior to 1948 and the provision of "good health for all from the cradle to the grave" is the result of setting up the NHS.

PENICILLIN, POLICEMEN AND WORCESTER ROYAL INFIRMARY

In 1943 the use of penicillin to treat infection was reserved for Allied servicemen. However, a policeman in the wards of Worcester Royal Infirmary did receive a course of this precious antibiotic. He had a massive carbuncle (a collection of boils) on the back of his neck. This was a debilitating and sometimes fatal infection. Wishing to provide optimum care, his surgeon – Mr Norman Duggan - applied to the military authorities for permission to use penicillin for a civilian. Permission was given and following treatment the policeman's infection cleared.

Earlier, in 1940, another policeman with streptococcal septicaemia was the first patient ever to be treated experimentally with this newly discovered antibiotic. His condition improved for four days, then sadly supplies ran out and he died.

In 1929 Alexander Fleming, a Scottish bacteriologist, published a paper identifying a 'mould' as 'penicillium rubrum' (actually p.notatum). He had been researching the bacteria (staphylococci) responsible for boils and carbuncles and recognized that colonies of bacteria had been destroyed by the 'mould'.

Unfortunately it was unstable and difficult to produce appreciable amounts. Also, although a strong and safe destroyer of Gram positive bacteria* (staphylococci, pneumococci diphtheria bacillus) it was not effective against Gram negative bacteria* (cholera). Thus interest was limited and no further development occurred at that time.

Fleming's work was reviewed ten years later by Ernest Chain, a refugee from Nazi Germany. He was a member of a team of Oxford scientists headed by Howard Florey. A biochemist in the team, Norman Heatley, devised improved production techniques and they were able to grow the penicillin in larger quantities. On the 25th

May 1940 they inoculated eight mice with fatal doses of streptococci. Four mice received penicillin and subsequently lived. Four mice, not treated, died.

Hence the attempt to treat a human patient – the policeman mentioned earlier.

These were early days of the war and British Pharmaceutical Companies were unable to aid production. Norman Heatley enlisted help from the USA at a laboratory in Illinois. They increased the yield 34-fold – made in beer vats !.

By 1943 however mass production of penicillin began in Britain and in May 1943 Howard Florey went to North Africa to use penicillin on wounded soldiers in the Africa Campaign. By D. Day in 1944 supplies were sufficient for all wounded Allied servicemen.

In 1938 building of an Emergency Medical Services Hospital was started in the rural area of Worcester at Ronkswood. It was completed early in 1942 and served wounded military from the battlefields of Europe. It accommodated, at the time, 800 patients in wards of 40 beds. When convalescent the patients were transferred to hospitals in Wales.

The nearby Shrub Hill Station assumed a new status as a junction for medical cases needing emergency treatment. Convoys of wounded soldiers arrived by train. Ronkswood Hospital received most of the casualties, having been purpose built. When full the overflow patients were treated at WRI Castle Street.

The pressure was intense and the twin operating theatres often had two operating tables in each, with two teams of operating staff to meet the needs of the injured men. Many of the casualties had limbs in plaster, the casts being labelled with their underlying injuries. The casts were removed, fractures reduced and wounds cleaned and sutured.

The limited supply of penicillin was used to treat these casualties. To enable the drug to be given post operatively capillary tubing was left in the suture lines.

W.H. McMenemey in his book, 'The History of Worcester Royal Infirmary', when describing conditions in World War II, said, "The corridors housed the wounded from France and other theatres of war, the ward accommodation being insufficient". He comments that "The infirmary has watched the earliest miracles of penicillin and seen the deadly germs of war wounds outmatched".

In the 21st century we are aware that use of penicillin, sulphonamides, blood transfusions, prophylactic inoculations were pioneering medical interventions just 60 / 70 years ago.

My thanks to miss M.E. Tarran, SRN SCM RCNT for the 1943 account of the 'Policeman & Penicillin'. She was a 3rd year student nurse in operating theatres at the time. Muriel Clayson

CHILDREN IN HOSPITAL

Although 'Bonaker Ward' was originally set up as a children's ward, it later was needed for the victims of the growing number of road accidents.

Duncan Carmichael, who comes from a long established Worcester family, was a patient in the children's ward in 1947 and writes:

This photograph (next page) shows me, far right, aged 5 at Christmas 1947 with two wonderful nurses at the Worcester Royal Infirmary. For more than three months one of these nurses would take me for a walk, most days, through the draughty corridors and down the cold stone staircase to the Jenny Lind Chapel.

There they would read me a story, usually from the Bible, before we retraced our steps 'upwards' back to the ward, which was no more than a corridor linking the new to the old hospital. My bed was in a window that looked down onto the Chapel.

The ward Duncan referred to was the E.N.T. ward, which was a series of rooms off a corridor above the Board Room.

So the need for a new children's ward was really urgent, and only four years later the two Bates children's wards were built. Bates Medical and Bates Surgical were purpose built in approximately 1951 and named after Tom Bates the Surgeon.

Bates Surgical catered for babies and children needing operations to correct congenital deformities, and victims of accidents. Appendicectomy was quite a common operation carried out on children.

CHILDRENS' WARD AT CHRISTMAS 1947 WITH TREE

Bates Medical catered for babies and children with infectious diseases and leukaemia, meningitis, burns and scalds and so on. Children with tonsil or ear conditions went to the Ears, Nose and Throat Ward – a separate ward in the old hospital.

The two Bates wards each included a variety of glass cubicles, so that newly admitted children could be screened for infectious diseases – every baby or child was carefully assessed so that no infections were spread to the very sick children already on the ward.

Epidemics of Whooping Cough, Polio, Scarlet Fever, Measles, Chicken Pox and so on were frequently raging round the city at that time. Barrier nursing was therefore extremely diligently carried out. I remember being soundly scolded because I managed to catch German Measles from a six year old boy.

Because the children tended to stay in Hospital for long periods, we became very fond of them and sometimes quite possessive. It can be hard to hand back a child you have spent weeks caring for, knowing that child will, through neglect at home, probably be re-admitted before long.

The Gypsy children were always a joy. The whole clan would come and camp on Pitchcroft and visit 'en masse'. One boy, Noah had been leading the horse-drawn caravan, when he slipped beneath the wheels, and both his legs were broken. He was a great character – happy and cheerful – in spite of everything.

Many children had serious congenital deformities. Such as cleft palate, club foot, and hydrocephalus, most of which could be corrected surgically.

Unfortunately the attitude of the hospital authorities at the time considered it a bad thing for parents to stay with their sick children, so the nurses had to adhere to these strict rules, and restrict visiting – very traumatic for all.

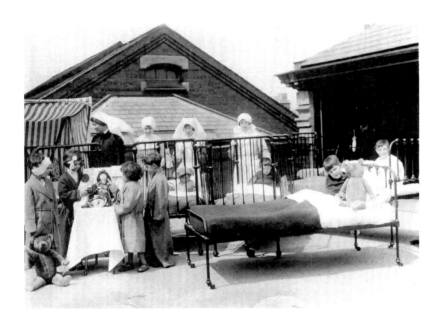

SUNNY EXTENSION TO CHILDRENS' WARD – C. 1930

The wards both had wide balconies so that some of the beds could be pushed outside on warm days and there was space for the children to play. A Teacher came in every day to help tutor some of the children, who may have been in hospital for months.

Christmas was always made very special for the children, with gifts, visits from Father Christmas and of course decorations and a tree. No one had the day off – all Nurses had to work all day in order to provide the best possible time for children in Hospital.

Probably one of the most dramatic procedures for tiny babies was surgery to cure pyloric stenosis. This is a congenital condition whereby the muscle layer surrounding the lower end of the stomach is too tight, like a rubber band, thus preventing the contents of the stomach passing through into the small intestine. The baby vomits violently and is liable to slowly starve to death. A simple nick in the 'rubber band' will solve the problem. But giving a tiny baby (usually boys) a general anaesthetic was far too risky. The baby was firmly bandaged to a padded cross – to uncurl him, it would be impossible otherwise – the baby was given a teat containing brandy and honey which he hungrily sucked – while the surgeon quickly made a small incision and then cut the 'rubber band'. It sounds really quite barbaric, but we never lost a baby, and there was no other choice if we wanted to save the life of that tiny baby.

CHILDRENS' PARTY IN 'OUTPATIENTS' – C. 1930

The milk kitchen was on Bates surgical and every day two nurses had to wash and sterilize all the feeding bottles and teats. Then the nurses had to make up the formula for each baby and toddler, for the following 24 hours, being careful to mark each bottle with the name of the patient. The feeds would then go in the fridge on the appropriate ward.

A much more unpleasant job for the night nurse at the end of their shift was to wash all the smelly nappies, which had been put into a large enamel bin containing a carbolic solution to kill all the bacteria. These were Terry nappies of course, no disposable nappies then!. Raw red hands were the result, and we had to complete this task just before going to our meal.

Caring for very sick children can be very distressing, but they are brave and cheerful and it is so rewarding to see them recover. We were always told not to become emotionally involved with our patients, but this is particularly difficult where children are concerned. Thankfully, children in Hospital are now cared for with their parents and siblings staying and even sleeping at their bedsides, a much more compassionate arrangement.

THE LAST MATRON MISS MAY HULME 1915 – 2009.

MISS MAY HULME (1915-2009), THE LAST MATRON

Miss Hulme will be remembered with great affection and respect by all who knew her. She was someone who cared a great deal about 'her' nurses, and strove to uphold the high standard of their training, and their care of the patients.

Fortunately she was interviewed for the Oral history Project so we have a great deal of information about her nursing life.

Born in 1915 in Oldham, the second daughter of Edward

and Cissy Hulme, her mother was the daughter of a wealthy Oldham merchant. After attending boarding school in Colwyn Bay, she had to choose between teaching science and nursing. As her Aunt had nursed in the 1914 – 18 war, she decided on nursing, and so trained at the Royal Lancaster Infirmary. She chose this Hospital because the probationers had their own Boat-House on the Lancaster canal.

After completing her training, earning £12 a year, she became a Theatre Staff Nurse in 1937 on £45 a year. Theatre was her main area of expertise.

In 1939 Miss Hulme undertook her 6 month midwifery training at the Liverpool Hospital, which was in the grounds of the Fever Hospital. They had had no infection for over 25 years.

During the war she longed to join the Navy or Air Force, but her poor eyesight prevented this. She then worked at Bury Hospital where she was Ward Sister, and then, in 1946, Theatre Superintendent. The hospitals were very strictly run and carefully assessed by the GNC (General Nursing Council).

In 1949 she moved south to take up the post of Night Superintendent at the Prince of Wales Hospital in Tottenham, and then Sister on a surgical ward, where she worked with Consultant Surgeon Mr Arthur Dixon-Wright, who was father to one of the 'two fat ladies' cooks. She undertook four months 'Admin Training' in Nottingham, which involved one month working in the laundry – quite an eye opener!

By the late 1940's the probationers were now referred to as 'student nurses' and the Block System of study was introduced. This was planned nationally by the G.N.C., including the exams. Her next move was to Burton Hospital where Miss Hulme was Theatre Superintendent for 3½ years. This was a well-run well equipped operating theatre with much emphasis on the value of 'nursing' in theatre. Great attention was paid to the wearing of uniforms, with neat hair kept in place with caps. Male nurses had to wear theatre caps on the wards. Because of this care there was no infection on the wards.

Although happy in Burton, Miss Hulme then moved to Stockport for one year as Senior Admin Sister and then on to Peterborough, where she was Deputy Matron over the group of 3 Hospitals, including a Fever Hospital of 66 special beds. Scarlet fever had died out by now, but there were many cases of Meningitis and Polio. Few died, all down to good nursing, and the help of God. Christian values were applied in many areas of nursing.

After three years as Deputy it was time to find a Matron's post. The interview at Worcester Royal Infirmary lasted two days – the first day included a tour of the two Hospitals. On the second day, the Board-room was packed with the management committee and all the senior medical, surgical and nursing staff. Mrs Porter was Chairman and many questions were asked including enquiring about Miss Hulme's attitude to uniform – they were delighted to hear that she was strict about their use. They said, "Woe betides the nursing profession if they ever get rid of caps"!. Then Miss Hulme was invited to ask questions; she asked what they would say if Matron wanted to attend Surgical Operations in theatre? Why?, they asked. Miss Hulme replied, "I would like to view nursing techniques and attitude". George Marshall replied, "Your idea is excellent, you will be welcome in my theatre any time".

Miss Hulme was offered the post and in October 1959 she commenced as the New Matron of Worcester Royal Infirmary. Miss Pearce, Assistant Matron, welcomed Miss Hulme, and introduced her to retiring Matron, Miss Healey, and the Ward Sisters. She wore her new uniform of dark blue silk with lace collar and cap. She found a "happy hospital" with a good teaching department, and nice uniform with caps.

There was no shortage of staff or money, with a "Brilliant Finance Officer". The finance committee gave advice to Matron, who was involved with decisions – everything ran well.

The Nurse training was excellent, and Matron always interviewed prospective students with their parents. Student Nurses would show the prospective student round the Hospital when they would hear interesting stories about Matron.

Miss Hulme had great respect for the Ward Sisters. After a ward round on Wheeley Lea Sister D.T. Brown said to Matron, "I'm surprised you didn't notice that speck of dust on the bed". Matron felt that the senior Sisters gave her strength – they were always very forthcoming at Castle Street, and they were all very experienced over many years. The Student Nurses also worked to a very high standard.

Miss Hulme really enjoyed Christmas. She usually sent her assistant to attend the dress rehearsal of the concert, in case there were any 'rude' bits.

The Jenny Lind Chapel played an important part in the life of the hospital. The Sanctuary Lamp needed cleaning and Olive the maid was asked to do this. It was suspended by a balance, and when the lamp was removed, the balance shot up to the ceiling. Miss Buckingham had to get the fire brigade in to retrieve the balance, in time for the WRI Nurses League Service. Matron thought this extremely amusing.

Miss Hulme retired from Worcester when the post became extinct in 1973. The staff sorely missed her benevolent presence, but she often attended the Nurses League re-union in May, so that she could keep contact with her ex-colleagues, and keep up to date with all that was happening in the profession.

Miss Hulme became a very prominent member of the little country Church of England Parish Church at Wicton, near Warton, and sometimes played the organ if required. She also helped in First Aid classes for the St. John's Ambulance and was active on the fund-raising committee for two local Hospitals, as well as her many kindnesses to her niece and nephews and their families.

She lived alone in Warton, near Preston, and suffered failing eyesight, but had good neighbours and family to care for her.

Eventually, Miss Hulme had to move into a care home where she was well cared for and visited by family. She sadly died in September 2009 after a very long life – lived to the full - and the last matron of Worcester Royal Infirmary.

REMARKABLE CHARACTERS

MR. GEORGE MARSHALL - GRATITUDE OF GENERATIONS TO AN EMINENT SURGEON

By kind permission of Michael Grundy

Only a rare few can make the same boast as one eminent Worcester personality that "he knew thousands of local people – inside and out"! Yet this is clearly the literal claim that could be jokingly made by the widely respected surgeon Mr George Marshall.

Numerous households in Worcester and a wide surrounding area will know of at least one member of their family – mother, father or grandparent – who underwent an operation at the hands of Mr Marshall. Many local people will have had cause to be deeply grateful for the life-saving or pain relieving skills of this remarkable and dedicated surgeon.

He said he had no idea how many operations he performed during 36 years as a surgeon at the Worcester Royal Infirmary, but by my rough calculations it must be about 30,000, and amazing though it may seem today, he performed the first 7,000 or so of those operations – FOR NOTHING!

Before the arrival of the National Health Service in 1948, surgeons were appointed to the staff of Worcester Royal Infirmary in a purely honorary capacity.

"Surgeon appointments at the Royal were keenly contested, and it was a great honour to be chosen. However, I suppose doctors today would think we were absolutely mad to take on all this extremely demanding surgical work and being paid nothing at all for it. There was no salary so it was essential to be in general practice too, as a family doctor, in order to make money to live", explained Mr Marshall.

His ambition was always to be a surgeon, and he looked back on his lifetime's career as having been memorable and rewarding. "In fact, I certainly did not want to give it up when I reached 65 but, alas, I had to do so because that's the rule". As a general surgeon he undertook a comprehensive range of operations, and in the latter part of his career he was recognised for particular accomplishments in cancer operations especially breast cancers.

Mr Marshall earned great respect from patients and colleagues alike. He was quite tall and well built, fairly quiet and dignified and rather intimidating to junior staff, but always had a twinkle in his eye. The most remarkable talent he had was his skill in diagnostics. Without the aid of modern 'tests', sometimes just a blood count would suffice, he was never wrong in his diagnosis! He had a great understanding of people, and a wonderful 'bed-side manner'.

He was a leader in the Medical Profession and was Chairman of both the Birmingham Regional Consultative Committee and Worcester Group Medical Committee.

Throughout his medical career, Mr Marshall considered midwifery, "Attending expectant mothers and helping at the birth of babies – was an especially rewarding and 'most important' facet of the work. If you can do that job properly, it shows that you are a good doctor".

GEORGE MARSHALL was born in Edinburgh in 1906 and both qualified in medicine and gained his FRCS (Fellow of the Royal College of Surgeons) in the Scottish capital. It was an advertisement in the British Medical Journal which brought him to Worcester in 1931 – to join the partnership of doctors 'Pollard & Rook' who had surgeries at 24, Foregate Street, and 51, Upper Tything. His true ambition to be a surgeon was realised in 1935 when he gained one of those coveted honorary posts at the Royal Infirmary, working six mornings a week and handling emergency work at some other times of day and night. He was what he describes as, "an old fashioned general practitioner surgeon", tackling all manner of operations.

Mr Marshall remembered standing-in one weekend for Nose & Throat specialist Bernard Cavanagh and dealing with a 'Colonel Blimp' type, who was admitted on the Sunday as an emergency with a bone stuck in his throat. "We got him into theatre, I removed the bone, which was well down, and I was rather pleased with myself. On the Monday morning, I went on the ward rounds with Bernard Cavanagh, and when we reached this particular patient, I told my colleague I had removed a rabbit bone from his throat. But the Colonel, clearly affronted, explained 'Damn it my boy, it was partridge!".

The outbreak of war brought huge demands on Mr Marshall's surgical work – day and night. In addition to his duties at the Royal Infirmary he was appointed surgeon to a special war-time emergency hospital which was set up in two big wards of the Powick Mental Hospital. Train loads of war wounded were brought to Worcester for treatment at the Infirmary and at the emergency hospital at Powick – and later at the one specially built at Ronkswood in 1941 which was run by its own separately appointed medical staff.

Mr Marshall recalled "wonderfully interesting": meetings which were held with leading American doctors and professors of medicine from Harvard who had come to deal with the wounded GI's at the cluster of US military hospitals set up at Malvern and other parts of Worcestershire. We heard some very fine lectures and formed what we called "The Vigornian Medical Society" for those meetings between ourselves and our American friends". From 1935 until the end of the war, Mr Marshall was also Medical Officer to the two Worcester Detachments of the British Red Cross.

The arrival of the National Health Service in 1948 signalled a major change in the career of Mr Marshall when he became a permanent salaried member of the surgical team at the Royal Infirmary, alongside such other leading surgeons as Tom Bates and Norman Duggan. It meant an operating theatre schedule of between three and six operations a day with between two and four emergency operations some nights.

As the years passed, the general practice of Pollard and Rook, which Mr Marshall had originally joined, became that of doctors Margaret Norton, Earle and Knowles.

MR. PAUL HOUGHTON, MR A.C. CLARK, MR. GEORGE MARSHALL, DR. KIDD, AND DR. RONNIE MATTHEWS, SENIOR MEDICAL STAFF AT HIS RETIREMENT IN 1971

Mr Marshall retired as a surgeon in 1971 and then set up a Medical Museum in the Post-graduate Centre at Ronkswood Hospital. It was filled with fascinating displays of medical instruments, curios and documents relating to surgery, medicine in general, pharmacy and veterinary skills. This collection formed the nucleus of the major collection of items on display at the George Marshall Medical Museum, housed in the Charles Hastings Education Centre at the Worcestershire Royal Hospital.

He retained 'a very soft spot' for the Royal Infirmary and was proud to have worked in this 18th century building where Worcester physician Sir Charles Hastings founded the British Medical Association in 1832.

Mr Marshall married Jill De Mierre, the twin sister of a leading Worcester dentist, in 1935, though he had been a widower for about 30 years. There are two children of the marriage – Sandy and Elizabeth.

As for that favourite sport of golf, Mr Marshall was County Champion in 1934 and played for Worcestershire until the beginning of the war. He certainly had no regrets at coming to Worcester more than 90 years ago, and spending his entire career in the City. However, his roots drew him back every year to holiday in East Lothian. He died peacefully, in his sleep, in March 2001.

MISS EVELYN LOUISE HEALEY MATRON – 1943 – 1959

A tribute from her niece – Miss Joanna Healey – December 1999.

I met Evelyn just over 10 years ago when she was already advanced in years. The woman I met, my grandfather's cousin, was an engaged lively and interested individual, who despite the increasing fragility of age, reached across the generations to me and offered friendship, companionship and above all else a sense of family.

Giving as much as she did, over the last 10 years – we were happy in those last few months of struggle to do whatever we could to help, to care and to comfort our Evelyn.

Thinking about the legacy that she has left us, and about who she was and what made her so special, the words of Mr W. Wright (Chairman of the Board of Management for Bexhill Hospital), written as a reference to the WRI, prior to her appointment, take on a new meaning. "MISS HEALEY – possesses the rare combination of a strong and at the same time charming personality with capability of a high order …. She had controlled her staff with a discipline which, though absolute, has earned her nothing but respect and affection… She has tackled with never failing energy, resource and good humour all the difficulties of war-time… In seeking the high standard of all-round efficiency, which she has attained, she had never spared herself."

MATRON EVELYN HEALEY PRESENTS LEAVING GIFTS TO ASSISTANT MATRON MISS BOWEN IN 1959

Seventeen years later, the Nursing Committee at the WRI wrote the following:

> *This committee place on record their sense of loss and regret at the retirement of Miss E.L. Healey —who in the finest traditions of her profession, has for 16 years filled the post of Matron of WRI with distinction and honour; their gratitude for her selfless, wholehearted and devoted service and for her watchful and unremitting care for the reputation and dignity of the hospital and its training school.*

Although these words were written half a century ago, to me they capture the essence of Evelyn: her dedication to service, her adherence to high ideal, her genuine and generous warmth, care and above else her wisdom. Most of us know that one of Evelyn's unique gifts was her ability to always have exactly the right advice and words of comfort in difficult times.

PRIZEGIVING 1958 – CENTRE FRON (SEATED) MATRON MISS HEALEY, STANDING AT THE CENTRE-BACK SISTER TUTOR MISS TURNER

Evelyn was not only the consummate professional and dutiful daughter and sister, but she was also a friend to most who knew her and a mentor to many.

SURGEON, LT. CDR. PAUL HOUGHTON.

BORN in London in 1911, Paul Houghton was educated at Whitgift School. As soon as he was old enough, his mother marched him up to Bart's Hospital to "do medicine".

At the beginning of World War II he worked at a Naval Hospital in Lowestoft. Although receiving no naval training he was sent to sea in 1941 to serve on the destroyer "Zulu" taking part in Atlantic convoys. He was expected to treat everything

LT. CDR PAUL HOUGHTON

from T.B. to burns and splinter wounds from blast damage. But amongst the worst casualties were survivors from the Ark Royal, who had flayed themselves as they slid down her hull covered in barnacles as she sank.

He joined a larger Battleship - Nelson in 1942, and he was appalled to be issued with long knives, saws and tarred string for tying off blood vessels, as issued in the days of Lord Nelson himself.

After requesting more modern equipment he was supplied with enough to supply the fleet! The Nelson was torpedoed, leaving Mr Houghton trapped in the dressing station. However, the ship survived and so did Mr Houghton, limping into Gibraltar.

In 1943 Mr Houghton performed an appendicectomy on Vice Admiral Neville Syfret in his sea cabin, saving his life. He also performed life-saving surgery on Rear Admiral Philip Vian.

After the war Mr Houghton worked in Shrewsbury General Hospital, where he met a pretty Wren – Jean Hallan Swift, he quickly proposed by saying, "What about you and me getting moored along-side?"

He was subsequently appointed Consultant General Surgeon in 1947 at Worcester Royal Infirmary – where he worked until his retirement in 1977, at the age of 66.

Mr Houghton was well known for playing practical jokes and on one occasion presented Miss Hulme (matron) with a birthday cake made from plaster of Paris. He was sometimes rather erratic in his behaviour in the Operating Theatre and would throw instruments on the floor, stating he certainly would not need any of them. Only to find a little later that they were the very instruments that were essential to his performing the surgery. In spite of this he was popular with his colleagues, and his sense of humour always shone through.

His strong Christian faith helped him throughout his long life, and he often prayed before operating on someone. After retirement he spent some time working in Hospitals with the African Mission and in the West Indies, also in Nazareth in Israel. He spent many hours working with his Wife in the running and serving the Church in Grimley, near Worcester – where he was Church Warden for many years.

Mr Houghton was held in great esteem by the many who knew him, and a huge congregation attended his funeral, when he died in August 2009 – a few weeks before his 98th birthday.

JOHN SMITH – THE MAN – THE NURSE

A tribute by Chaplain Jacqui Hughes

MR JOHN SMITH (RIGHT) PRESENTING ORTHOPAEDIC SURGEON MR. A.C. CLARKE WITH HIS LEAVING GIFT 1970

John never got round to writing his book – "Dawn at Shrub Hill" but the tales he had to tell were legendary.

He was in his early twenties when he left home in St. John's for the first time to do his military service. The camp at Beckett's Park – Leeds, sharing barracks with other chaps. The boots – Army Boots, the regulation hair cut! – were not quite his scene.

John joined the Medical Corps as a Theatre Orderly (there were no male nurses then). He had found his vocation in life – like a duck to water!

He was already kitted-out for India when a skin condition prevented him from leaving for the tropics – so the northern hemisphere was the location for John's war-time experience - Northern Ireland, the

Shetlands and Hospital Ships. Casualties from the North Atlantic convoys kept the Hospital Ships busy, hours and days on end in the Operating Theatre. Sixty years on John still had friends from the war years.

After the war John did his nurses training in London and due to his war service it was a shortened course and then he returned to his beloved Worcester. He was the first male nurse to work at the Worcester Royal Infirmary. Matron only took him on a three month trial – and he stayed for 43 years!.

The Operating Theatre is by nature separate from the rest of the hospital and the main stream of hospital life, so John's work was only witnessed by colleagues in Theatre……. Here are some quotes :-

"He was an artist in the profession of 'Theatre Nurse' – he turned it into an art-form. What drama and style he had" !

"He was so good that the young students held him in great awe…… To see John scrub-up was memorable" !

"He took his work very seriously, indeed he was a perfectionist and had a talent for passing on his high standard and professionalism".

"He inspired others to follow in his footsteps, setting a good example to everyone".

John gave support to all his colleagues – he was always there when individuals needed him. He had time for everyone. People would go to John with a personal problem – he would listen in such a way as to enable them often to solve their own problems.

He never criticized people, nobody disliked him. He could be infuriating, but you couldn't be cross with him for long. John was a great teller of tales – his observations of people were hilarious and recollections of events and dates were always in great detail. His memories went back a long way and John kept in touch with friends all over the world.

From early childhood John enjoyed the boats on the river Severn, but his first cruise was on a Banana Boat! Later he progressed to cruising on the great liners, especially the QE II – he had many tales to tell about that!

John had style – Taxi and first class travel wherever he went – the only way to travel he thought. In any case, 1st class usually included a free cup of tea and a newspaper. Many of his favourite tales were of the wonderful times he had at the Annual Chelsea Arts Ball!

His interests were many – reading, gardening, the theatre – John had a huge collection of Theatre Programmes - and of course travelling. John was a wonderful host – a very good cook. Many would have enjoyed John's hospitality – if only a cup of coffee and a better class of biscuit. "Can you visualize John sitting cross-legged, cigarette in one hand and a large Gin & Tonic in the other, laughing at another tale just recounted".

"Let's hope there's a cocktail bar in heaven where John can chat with his friends".

John was unique, as a friend he had no equal - a gentle gentleman.

DOCTOR OLAF PÜLBERG

OLAF was always an enigmatic character shrouded in mystery.

Born one fine winter's day in 1914 in St. Petersburg the family were forced to flee the troubled City and made their way back to their homeland – Estonia.

Olaf attended Tallin University where he graduated in Medicine in 1941. The Germans had invaded and occupied Estonia, and Olaf was forced to a labour camp and then sent as a Medical Officer in the German Army – to fight on the Russian Front.

By 1947 he was a refugee and came to England where he was trained to work in the Yorkshire coal-mines, unable to prove his Medical qualifications until later.

In 1951 he came to Worcester where he worked in A/E and then was appointed resident Anaesthetist. He always seemed to be working, night and day, standing in for colleagues and volunteering for extra duties. He never said much but had a wicked sense of humour – allegedly spiking the drinks at the Christmas Party.

A very heavy smoker, pacing up and down the corridors, it's a wonder he didn't blow the whole place up with all the anaesthetic gases used in the 1950's. It was said he furnished his flat with things bought with cigarette coupons!

In 1968 Olaf married Nurse Frances Gillard, who was only 28 years old and they had two children. In 1983 Olaf finally retired and he and the family moved to St. Johns.

After so many years in England he became a British National in 1992; he travelled back to Estonia, which had recently become independent. To his great distress, after being away for over 50 years there was no trace of his home or family, just a few graves. His grandparents had been shipped off to Siberia, never to be seen again.

Olaf died in May 2007 after a long well deserved retirement, in his 93rd year.

KATHLEEN HARRISON – ELGAR'S PRIVATE NURSE

For Kathleen Harrison, the pinnacle of her lengthy career in the Nursing profession was perhaps reached when she nursed composer Sir Edward Elgar through his last five months of life.

It was in October 1933 that Elgar was admitted to South Bank Nursing Home, then part of Worcester Royal Infirmary. He was 76 and had been suffering from severe back pains, which were thought to be sciatica. He was known to be somewhat of a hypochondriac, so, sadly, no one took a great deal of notice. However, exploratory surgery at South Bank revealed that the composer had inoperable cancer of the bowel.

He was so very ill and not expected to survive, so as he was Catholic, the Last Rites were read to him. Kathleen Harrison, then working as a Sister at South Bank, was invited by the Matron and Elgar's daughter Carice to be Sir Edward's special Nurse, under the direction of his physician, Dr. W.E. Moore-Ede.

One day while Kathleen was massaging Elgar's back, he said to her, "My dear, I may be a troublesome old man, but I am in a lot of pain you know". He held out his hand and said, "You'll never leave me will you?" "Never", Kathleen replied!

She nursed him at South Bank for three months, and then at his home, Marlbank, Rainbow Hill, where he was taken in January 1934.

His room was cluttered with "electrical contraptions", which was equipment to enable Elgar direct access to the Abbey Road Recording Studios in London, so that he could supervise the recording of all his music, the first composer to do so. Elgar struggled through pain and the effect of morphia to complete the huge project.

"He had been on pain-killers all the time, he suffered such agonising pain – I was there with him on February 23rd 1934 – when he just died. It was the middle of the night – he didn't say anything – I was with him all the time". Such had been her devotion to caring for Sir Edward in his last months that she was privileged to be among only about 20 close friends and relatives who were invited to attend his quiet private funeral at St. Wulstan's Roman Catholic Church in Little Malvern.

Kathleen's nephew – John Harrison said, "My Aunt was sad that Elgar had never recovered sufficiently to fulfil a promise to take her by car round his favourite haunts in the Worcestershire countryside". "She used to talk too of his music and remembered him sometimes calling for his notepad when he wanted to jot down musical notes". It seems she got on well with Elgar's daughter Carice too, and would sometimes join her in the evening for a sherry and a cigarette, as partial respite from caring for the dying composer.

Born in 1896 in Albany Road, Rainbow Hill, Kathleen was a local girl who trained as a Nurse at Worcester Royal Infirmary. Following Elgar's death she worked in Hospitals in Birmingham, Wolverhampton and Bath where she was a Theatre Sister. In the 1940's she was Matron of Berkeley's Hospital in the Foregate – with responsibility for Alms houses in the Butts, Nash's Passage and Laslettes. Kathleen was very much a Nurse of the "Old School" – forthright of manner, and strict, but always extremely caring.

In retirement Kathleen lived in Warden-supervised accommodation in Barbourne and then in her later years was a resident of 'The Lawns' at Kempsey.

She died in 1992 at the grand age of 96 – after a long and active life.

N.B. – Her nephew John Harrison worked as a porter at Worcester Royal Infirmary for 20 years – many staff would remember him.

MEMORIES

FRANCES ETHEL BROWN ("F.E.") 1907 - 2005

FRANCES ETHEL BROWN (2ND FROM LEFT) IN 1940

Written by a niece of F.E

My Aunt Frances was a remarkable lady from a remarkable family and had a very long, interesting and rewarding life.

Her father (my grandfather) was born in 1845, a Somerset farmer's son who became a greatly respected business man in Bridgewater and died in 1937 at the age of 92. He married three times and Frances was the 11th of his 13 much loved children.

She was born at home in Bridgewater in February 1907 and in due course went to boarding school at Clifton High School in Bristol. In 1922, at the age of 15, after her Mother went into a long-term nursing home she was recalled to manage the family home, a very large old house with a cook and servants.

It was obviously a difficult time for a 15 year old supervising the staff who were not best pleased with the arrangement. I remember her showing me a schedule she had made - 7 o'clock - cup of tea for Mr Brown, breakfast sharp at 8, rooms to be dusted, beds made, lunch prompt at 1 o'clock etc., etc., but she managed it very well and coped with all the family visits as well.

Her methodical attention to detail helped her nursing career later on, I'm sure.

She was always very fond of tennis and in the fashion of the twenties always served 'underarm' - and very effective it was too! However, around 1931 she decided she should get an outside profession and let her younger sister run the house, so at the age of 24 she became a nurse at Bristol General Hospital.

She found studying hard work so long after leaving school but in 1936 won the Bristol General Hospital Silver Medal for her work, and became a Ward Sister - a bit of a Dragon, I suspect! Strict with the Nurses - nobody left the building without changing out of uniform! Wards spotlessly clean and Matron in overall charge etc., etc.

When the war came to Bristol, and the Blitz, she was involved in moving her patients - in their beds - down to the basement. The Hospital was hit with a bomb one night but it did not explode, and when examined later, was found to have been made in Czechoslovakia and filled with sand instead of explosives.

As the war went on, Frances became due to be conscripted, and after some training with the Queen Alexandra's Nurses, along with others went by ship, round the Cape of Good Hope and through the Suez Canal to an Army Hospital in Alexandria. This was at the time when General Montgomery and the British 8th Army were fighting the North Africa Campaign against the Germans under Rommel. Our wounded were being sent back to the Hospital in Alexandria. This would be during 1942 / 43 period and the Battle of El Alamein.

After this, the nurses followed the 8th Army across the Med. and up through Italy. A time of tented Hospitals and extremely difficult conditions - dirt, flies, bugs and creepy crawlies to be dealt with, plus - of course - the wounded. Frances celebrated V. E. Day in Florence, one of the high spots for her.

During this time in Egypt and Italy she wrote copious letters home, that is, to her older sister, my Mother - our house had become 'home' for her in Bristol. These letters, on flimsy war-time air-mail paper, were full of fascinating details of her life and that of her colleagues, the nursing they had to do, the conditions with which they had to contend daily, what they did for entertainment and relaxation and so on. My Mother kept all these letters together for any of the family to read and they were really like a book about the lives of Nurses overseas in the war. More recently they were offered to the Imperial War Museum and gratefully accepted and filed by the Archivist for the benefit of future researchers.

After demobilisation Frances became a Ward Sister at Worcester Royal Infirmary. specialising in orthopaedics, but gradually as time went by she began to suffer from arthritis in her hips, and both were operated on - twice - by 'the' Mr Charnley, in the pioneering days of hip replacements and later she had a shoulder which required an operation also. During this period she suffered dreadful pain. She retired to a delightful ground-floor flat at Barbourne in Worcester, a complete change from living in the nurses' home in Hospital. She could have visitors and cook, and grow flowers in her tiny garden - she was very proud of her roses.

She had numerous interests - she had a little car which gave her a lot of pleasure. She was very well read, very interested in wildlife, especially birds and loved to visit 'hides' and make lists of 'sightings' when on holiday, together with enjoying good music and concerts. Eventually the time came when being alone in her much loved flat became too difficult, so in 1997 she moved into the excellent Dorset House Home in Droitwich where she was very well cared for.

Sadly, as the years moved on her eyesight, hearing and mobility deteriorated until she was unable to read her books or hear her tapes and "Talking Books for the Blind". She took up crossword puzzles in a courageous fight to keep her mind active. Clues were written down for her in very large felt-tip pen letters and discussed with friends and relations during visits or telephone calls, as long as she was able.

The family was very important to her. Belonging to such a large 'Brown' family, Frances had a host of brothers and sisters, with nephews and nieces galore, and a multitude of cousins. They (we) were all very important to her and she was always interested in news of us and visits when possible.

She also had made many local friends, some of whom had been Nurses or Doctors with her at Worcester. Frances always had a very strong Christian faith and remained a member of Worcester Baptist Church to the end.

She will be greatly missed and long remembered by the family and everyone who knew her.

WARTIME MEMORIES BY FRANCES E. BROWN

Ward Sister – Bonaker Ward (1950 – 1972)

I joined the Queen Alexandra Nurses Reserve after the Hospital, where I was working in Bristol, was bombed and I was called up in 1942.

I went on a troop ship to Egypt which took 10 weeks. At the Red Sea the two Destroyers left us and we were defenceless. It was very hot and we slept on deck. We were bombed by depth charges and ordered on deck with our life-belts, which we always had to carry. In my hurry I arrived on deck with a toilet roll. I never lived that down! Luckily we weren't hit.

In Cairo I was appointed to a Desert Hospital. There was a main hut serving food and we had to go and bring the food to the smaller huts. If we didn't have a male orderly with us the vultures would swoop down and take the meat off the plates. There was diphtheria, typhoid, scarlet fever, enteritis and TB patients – all soldiers – in different huts. How we managed to escape infection I do not know.

Then I was posted to Alexandria. The Germans were only 40 miles away when 'Monty' took charge. I was in the 8th Army – so much happened. I was 18 months in Egypt, then sent on to Italy.

I was Sister on a small mobile Hospital with one driver and one mate – leapfrogging from one Hospital to another. We followed the Germans as they were retreating looking after the wounded on the way from Castelmare overlooking the bay of Naples. There we saw Vesuvius erupt – very frightening – flames, smoke and a terrible noise. Rome was a free City and wasn't bombed. I remember sitting in a cornfield waiting to go in. Everywhere we went – hospitals, houses, schools – just everywhere they could the Germans had filled all the pipes with cement so that there wasn't any plumbing for toilets etc.,. I was on leave in Florence and was there for V.E. Day and had a wonderful Service.

I was then posted to Greece for three months, then flown back from Naples to Peterborough in a Lancaster Bomber. This took just 10 hours, travelling in the bomb-racks, with just a bucket behind a curtain. I thought I had never seen anything so wonderful as the green grass, especially as the plane I should have travelled on was 'lost at sea'.

I came to Worcester in 1946 and commenced work in Battenhall Ward – with 10 or 12 beds.

Battenhall Ward was situated in the basement of the new block containing the Operating Theatres. Sister F.E. Brown was in charge of the ward which cared for male orthopaedic patients and transferred with them to Bonaker ward in 1951. The children from Bonaker ward were transferred to the newly opened Bates Medical and Bates Surgical wards at the same time. The redundant Battenhall ward then became a classroom for the teaching of practical nursing to the student nurses.

THE BOARD ROOM TABLE

THE BOARD ROOM TABLE IN C. 1965. LEFT TO RIGHT SEATED – MISS
NANCY DORRELL, MRS INEZ SPALDING, MRS CHRISTINE DORRELL. GEORGE
MARSHALL IS THIRD FROM LEFT, STANDING AND DR MICHAEL ATKINSON
IS FAR RIGHT.

This rather humble-looking table is possibly the one which stood in
the Board Room at the Worcester Infirmary in the 19th Century.
Alderman Dr. Frederick Spalding, an eminent 20th Century local
Doctor, claims that this could be the table on which the signing and
founding of the BMA took place in 1832 at the Infirmary. He was in
General Practice in Worcester and is also listed in 'McMenemy' as
House Physician in 1914, Anaesthetist in 1919, Pathologist in 1920
and even Gynaecologist in 1930, so he was a man of many talents.
Eventually he was appointed Consultant Physician to Worcester
Royal Infirmary in the 1940s. Alderman Spalding was Mayor of
Worcester in 1954 and was awarded the Freedom of the City in
1962.

The table is of a light mahogany colour with bulbous legs, and has two extra leaves to extend the length. It was acquired by Alderman Dr. Spalding for his practice in Foregate Street following the purchase of a much larger table for the infirmary board room in the 1930's. Apparently his wife, Mrs Inez Spalding, had her tonsils removed on this very table at the Foregate Street surgery.

In 1946 when Dr. Spalding retired and moved out of the premises in Foregate Street, the table was acquired by his friend Miss Nancy Dorrell for the new board room in the Russell & Dorrell Northwick Factory (latterly Faithful Overalls) where it stayed until 1965. Modernisation of the premises meant that the table became redundant.

Mrs Christine Dorrell, sister-in-law of Nancy Dorrell, was a friend of Dr Michael Atkinson, who at that time was Medical Superintendent of the Postgraduate Centre at Ronkswood Hospital. They arranged for the table to be available on a long loan to the Postgraduate Centre.

When Ronkswood Hospital was closed in 2002, the table was transferred to the Charles Hastings Education Centre at the new Worcestershire Royal Hospital, where it is now on permanent display as part of the George Marshall Medical Museum.

Many momentous decisions must have been made around this table over the centuries and many famous signatures inscribed. If only it could talk, what tales it would tell!

THE "FRIENDS" AND THE INFIRMARY BUFFET

By Doris Kershaw – Past Buffet Chairman.

DORIS KERSHAW AND JILL STRUDWICK, BUFFET VOLUNTEERS

In November 1935, the first Worcester Royal Infirmary Buffet made its appearance at Castle Street, opening on certain days of the week, when the Out-Patients Department was at its busiest.

WRI was a voluntary hospital, continually troubled with a huge overdraft at the bank, occasionally obliged to close a ward as a temporary economy and relying almost entirely on voluntary contributions. At this time of acute anxiety, an appeal was broadcast one Sunday on the BBC radio by the Lord Bishop of Worcester, the Right Rev. A.W. Perowne, who was also the President of the Infirmary. This was followed by a letter of appeal delivered next day to every household in the City and the County.

This led to the formation of the Worcester Royal Infirmary Women's Auxiliary Association, with Lady Atkins as Chairman. Their objects were to provide linen and to assist in promoting functions for the benefit of the Infirmary, especially for the Matron.

This lady, the much loved Miss Elsie Perry, after consultation with Lady Atkins, suggested a buffet or tea-bar in the out-patients hall, to sell cups of tea and biscuits to all comers. There was no café within easy reach, many out-patients came long distances and the out-patients hall was then a cold and draughty place.

For the modest sum of one old penny, patients and their waiting friends could purchase a cup of tea and a biscuit. There were no frills about the initial buffet - just a table with crocks and a teapot. No water or heat was laid on and, when more tea was required, a helper had to retire to the main hospital kitchen to make another pot.

The late Miss Valentine Noake recalled how 'official' recognition suddenly came. Mr Tom Bates, Senior Hon. Surgeon and a formidable personality, crossed the hall with house surgeon in attendance and halted at the table. Helpers held their breath "Tea", said Mr Bates loudly "Will you have a cup?" The house surgeon agreed and the approval of Mr Bates was just what the helpers needed. If 'he' said yes, then all was well.

It was also recalled that gypsies camping on Pitchcroft used to bring their babies' bottles to be filled with milk and to be warmed in the washing up bowl.

When the NHS came into being in 1948 the Women's Auxiliary Association was disbanded, but the buffet continued under the newly formed Friends of the Worcester Royal Infirmary as 'The Guild of Helpers of WRI buffet'.

In the annual report of the WRI for 1935, it was recorded that in their first year the Women's Auxiliary provided six pair of sheets, six cot blankets, three dozen towels, three dozen pillowcases, sundry articles for Bonaker Ward and quilts for Garlick Ward.

Profit in the first year of trading was £35. The Castle Street Buffet continued to give a service to out-patients, visitors and staff, and donated to Worcester Hospitals, through the Friends, between £4,000 and £5,000 each year.

In 2000 the Friends of WRI made grants of £163,884 – to the Castle Street, Ronkswood and Newtown hospitals - providing equipment for patient care. £100,000 was given to The Charles Hastings Education Centre.

Members of the Buffet were all volunteers, eighty regular helpers, both ladies and gentlemen and ten reserves. Some had served between 30 and 45 years each.

Besides helping at the 50th Anniversary of the NHS celebration in the Old Bishop's Palace, I was delighted, with my husband, to represent the Buffet helpers at the Royal Garden Party for the NHS in 1998. There we were introduced to Her Majesty the Queen who was interested that we were named Friends of the Royal Infirmary. Having explained that the WRI had celebrated 250 years of caring in the City and that the original Infirmary had been built in 1746 in Silver Street, transferring to Castle Street in 1771, Her Majesty wished us well and said that we deserved a new hospital! We were delighted that the hospital was named the Worcestershire Royal Hospital.

The Buffet was always open, the dedication and loyalty of the helpers being quite unique. The longest serving members were Mrs Hepworth (45 years) and Mrs Brooks (40 years). I might add at this stage that I am close behind, having contributed 39 years' service to the Hospital, jointly with the Buffet in Castle Street and as a committee member of WRH.

However, I am yet to beat one of our members, Mrs Wade, who aged 82, made her way through the famous year 2000 flood to go on duty. The hospital was waterlogged and closed but she stayed, serving tea to the emergency services.

The 'Friends of WRI' became the 'Friends of WRH'. Now they hold an annual bazaar in the new hospital, arrange coffee mornings, sell Christmas Cards and run a stall at Worcester's Victorian Fayre, together with regular collections in shops and supermarkets. In 2007 they donated £52,275 – in grants for patient comforts and medical equipment.

In October 2001, a farewell gathering of the WRI Buffet Helpers was held in the Board Room. This was attended by the Deputy Mayor, Councillor Robert Rowland and the Chairman of the Worcestershire Acute Hospitals NHS Trust, Mr Harold Musgrove, and about 70 members past and present.

It would be impossible to calculate how many cups of tea and reassuring words have passed over the hospital's buffet counter since its humble beginnings. In over 66 years it provided a valuable support for both patients and staff, and would not have done so but for the tireless voluntary support of its helpers.

I am most grateful to the late Mr George H. Marshall F.R.C.S. and the late Miss Valentine Noake who kindly provided much of the material on the early history of the Buffet.

FORTY THREE YEARS IN PATHOLOGY

COLIN LEGGE – Head Biomedical Scientist in Haematology retired in March 2002 after 43 dedicated years at Worcester, both at Castle Street and Ronkswood. Before he left, he penned in his own words, how things had changed in Haematology and the Health Service during his time at Worcester.

MR. COLIN LEGGE - HEAD BIOMEDICAL SCIENTIST IN HAEMATOLOGY (2002)

FROM STEAM TO SILICON

January 1st 1958 – (not a Bank Holiday then) was my first day at WRI. Parked my bike where the old X-ray Department was at Castle Street. Never bothered to lock anything up. Only three people had cars in the Department then – two Pathologists and Brian Savage, a senior in Haematology.

He and several other male staff had just returned from National Service and seemed very bright, clever and boffin-like, just like the masters at school. Microbiology was run on military lines by Colonel R.I. Henderson – surnames only. Histology and Haematology were entrusted to Drs. Patrick Kidd and Felix Kurrein. Dr. Humphrey Fawns was head of Biochemistry. There were about 25 staff altogether.

One worked, studied and trained in all four disciplines in those days, often swopping from one lab to another in the same day depending on what needed doing. (Multitasking – done that!). A stint of duty at St. Wulstan's Hospital – Malvern was an experience – working in a Regional TB Centre populated with people from Birmingham and the Black Country with different accents. I used to cycle there in the summer and claim 19s6d (98p) monthly expenses. My salary was a princely - £224 – per annum. Training and examinations took place at the Birmingham University Medical School, which took half a day to get there on the 144 bus, back home for midnight.

Fun was in the form of dances in the Nurse's Recreation Room (afterwards – Medical Records Library at CSB) and transportation was by bike or latterly motor-bike. Participation in the 'Christmas Show' was compulsory and I played the piano for budding Pop-Stars in front of a packed house consisting of Nurses, Consultants and Matron. I don't think she always approved of our antics or the jokes, but we thought it hilarious.

Most laboratory equipment was reusable. Some of it still labelled "US Army" – relics of World War II. Washing glass flasks, cylinders and pipettes was a major part of an afternoon's work. Sinks full of hot water, steam, Sulphuric Acid – marvellous!. I had lovely clean nails for a 17 year old. Air-conditioning – was opening the window, overlooking H.A. Saunders Garage in Castle Street, and loosening the tie!.

The Sixties saw a huge expansion in Medical Laboratories. More room, more staff and new equipment. With the seventies came electronics and automated analysers to cope with the ever increasing workload. Haematology and Biochemistry were relocated to Ronkswood. Everything needed a Silicon Chip to work it.

Computers took over in the Eighties and got much more sophisticated in the Nineties. Workloads soared – pay-slips didn't!. Now practically everything is disposable. The diagnosis and treatment of patients has become very sophisticated. Staff are educated up to MSc level and analysers are highly complicated *machines requiring long and arduous training courses for the staff running them. Total staff now approaching 160. Now computers rule – mobile phones, e-mail, Internets, Digital Cameras, Satellites, LANS, LIMS, PCR, Transplants and Silicon Chips everywhere. Where will it all end?*

Colin Legge – 2002.

THE OPERATING THEATRE – 1950's STYLE

Today's Theatre Sisters would hardly recognise the conditions existing 60 years ago, which were common in the training of a Theatre Nurse.

Every student nurse was required to spend 12 weeks basic training – in either Theatre or A&E Nursing. There was no choice, and if you were sent to theatre it was truly a baptism of fire.

Many people hated theatre because the conditions were quite appalling. The preparation of instruments and equipment was carried out in the sterilizing room – which was a cross between Hell and a Chinese Laundry – with great cauldrons of boiling water sterilizing everything, creating huge clouds of steam – one could not see across the room. Sterilization, in boiling water, had to be for at least 20 minutes – 19 minutes and the process had to start all over again.

Many people were scarred for life by boiling water streaming from trays of instruments carried into the theatre – where the Surgeons were waiting impatiently. Anything sharp had to be sterilized by immersion in Lysol – an evil thick brown caustic liquid, which again left scars from severe burns.

Everything was recycled – washed, dried, patched, repaired and sterilized – including gloves, masks, gowns, needles, syringes, drapes, tubing, catheters etc., which was extremely labour intensive, and of course mostly carried out by the slaves – sorry – student nurses. All this for a salary of £6 per month!!

Every evening all the Surgeons socks and shoes had to be washed and whitened then hung out of the window to dry. The theatre and side rooms were all scrubbed clean – again by the students and staff nurses. On Sundays, when there were no lists of operations, the instruments and the drains were minutely scraped of any lime deposits.

Then came the day when you were allowed to "scrub-up" always under supervision, for George Marshall, the most senior consultant. He was a tall and rather daunting figure – at least he seemed that way to a short, petrified student nurse – and suddenly all the trials and tribulations seemed worth it; learning the instruments and techniques of each Surgeon, performing many kinds of surgery was very challenging but rewarding. The discipline was very strict indeed and the hierarchy adhered to.

A student nurse was not allowed to speak to a surgeon, or even a senior nurse, unless they spoke first. The Theatre Superintendent was very much in charge – she was often to be found at her desk in the office, chain–smoking her Piccadilly cigarettes while stitching Tonsil swabs – but she knew everything that was happening in her department.

You had to be a fast learner and be very fit in order to keep up with the pace of work. Teamwork and knowing your place in the team was a valuable lesson a student learnt.

But perhaps the most valuable lesson was that each patient under your care trusted you to put their welfare first while anaesthetized and undergoing surgery. The Theatre Nurse is the patients advocate when he is most vulnerable – each patient should be treated as you would treat your own mother, brother or child. This is as true today as it was 60 years ago.

THE OPERATING THEATRE 1910

GHOSTLY GOINGS ON

Many nurses on Night Duty have told tales of mysterious shady figures, odd reflections and sometimes 'cold patches' usually on the Bates Wards, which strangely are the newest Wards in the hospital!

For instance – Linda Randall told me she had heard Tom Bates, who wore a Top Hat, when he walked the corridors of the children's wards.

Hazel Thomas remembered feeling very 'spooked' on Bates Medical – "I was on 'nights' and the other nurses had gone for a break. There was an area at the back of the ward, which was like a play place in the day for the children. This particular night the door suddenly opened wide to the play area and then closed with a bang. I looked up and saw a shape walking on the other side of the (glass) door. I went to investigate, opened the door and looked into the play area, there was nobody there.

No one could have got past me without me seeing them!. The room felt very cold and I had prickles up my spine. I was later told, when I mentioned the occurrence to colleagues, that a few other people had experienced a similar event on that particular ward. I never felt threatened, but I was never comfortable when on 'night duty' after that".

The Operating Theatres might not seem the obvious setting for Ghostly presences, but in the dead of night when the day's surgery and all the emergencies have been dealt with, the routine chores are carried out. Only essential lights are left burning, the main theatre darkly menacing – waiting for the next tragedy to unfold.

A daily stocktaking of all sterile packs of swabs and bandages etc., is carried out in the pack-room, which is lined from floor to ceiling with shelves of packs.

Sometimes, when I was alone in the theatre, perched on the top of tall step-ladders busy counting the packs, I would suddenly go cold (the theatres are usually kept very warm) and then hear 'heavy breathing', very close, over my shoulder. In the silence it sounded very scary, so I would frantically climb down the ladders as quickly as possible and race out of the theatre....... This happened to other people too.

Another rather strange thing was the very heavy wooden sliding doors on the pharmacy cupboard in the theatre corridor would sometimes 'slide open' or 'slide closed' on their own, when no one else was present. The distinctive sound of the doors sliding – on brass rollers – could be heard loud and clear from the next room, but there was never any one there when we investigated.

Sometimes I would clearly hear my name called from the next room, but no one was ever there.

Once the Hospital had been vacated in 2002, the building was looked after by a Security Firm, to prevent any vandalism.

The Officers on duty report several strange incidents occurring – including lights going on and off in Mulberry House and the main Hospital building. Doors were heard being slammed shut when no-one was there, and stiff sash windows opened on their own.

In the office behind the reception desk a "pair of hands" has been seen 'passing through the room'.

Maybe the strangest of all was when a security officer opened his office door to find the room full of people. Apologising for the interruption he quickly closed the door thinking he had disturbed a meeting. Returning half an hour later he discovered no meeting had been held, only his colleague had been alone in the room for the last few hours.

Pauline Shuker tells me she was on 'Night Duty' on Rushout Ward in 1964 – she says, "My Ghost visited the main ward most nights, but not every night. The time would be between 12 midnight and 2.00am, and always when I was the only nurse on the ward – my co-nurse having gone for her break. I was usually in the office, when I would hear the main ward door open – then click shut, followed by the sound of footsteps leading to the kitchen, then the sound of the door opening and closing shut.

I would wait anxiously for my colleague's return, then we would creep down to the kitchen – fling open the door, but of course no-one was there. I tried several times to "catch" my invisible visitor – all to no avail.

THE BIG MOVE

After 231 years, the Royal Infirmary in Castle Street finally closed.

On Sunday March 24th 2002 the last patients were transferred into the new Worcestershire Royal Hospital at Newtown on the eastern outskirts of Worcester.

The historic move was said to have gone without a hitch. The move was the biggest logistical operation the county had ever seen, and posed a huge challenge for the eighty-strong team of Ambulance workers and volunteers.

The experience could have been very traumatic for the patients but because of the extreme care, good humour and patience of the ambulance staff, always conscious of treating each patient with respect, they were all transferred without any problems.

It was a day long awaited since talk of a new hospital was instituted in the 1950's – when everyone recognized that the Georgian building was no longer suitable to carry on modern medicine. But when the day arrived to vacate the dear old place, there were many tears, and staff who had worked there for many years were reluctant to leave – not really knowing for sure what the future held for the building. Many were afraid that the building would be demolished.

Happy memories came flooding back as not only the nurses, but all the other staff, doctors, porters, cooks, secretaries, radiographers, physiotherapists etc., bade a tearful farewell to the familiar, well-loved ancient buildings that held such a wealth of history.

A service of thanksgiving for the hospital and its entire staff was held in the Jenny Lind Chapel on the 3rd March 2002, a very moving occasion.

At the auction sale soon after the closure, much of the equipment, like beds, trolleys, lockers and electrical equipment was bought by the Worcester Rotary Clubs for use in African Hospitals. The items in the Chapel like the Sanctuary Lamp were rescued by the Nurses League and are kept in the George Marshall Medical Museum.

REBIRTH

UNIVERSITY OF WORCESTER CITY CAMPUS

The University Of Worcester has taken over the hospital buildings in Castle Street as part of its City Campus. The Georgian building has been returned to life as the new home of Worcester Business School which reopened in September 2010.and the City Campus is a dramatic fusion of old and new architecture.

The University have done a wonderful job in renovating and restoring the original 1771 building, the Chapel and Mulberry House. Everything has been stripped back to the original fabric, and even the old Georgian glass has been preserved.

The former Out-patients Hall has become a beautiful open space, and none of the wards have been divided into small rooms. The outside brickwork has all been repaired and some of the external areas including the Chapel have been exposed to view for the first time for over 80 years. It all looks really beautiful, spacious, elegant and back to its former glory.

A new feature in the restored buildings is the McClelland Centre for Health and Well Being, which is named after Miss Mary Jane

McClelland, the matron who established the nurses' library at the WRI.

All the other structures of the former WRI have been demolished including the 1932 Nurses Home and extensions, and the Georgian Walnut Tree House, which had previously been the Earl of Coventry's Town House.

EXHIBITION

By Catriona Smellie, Curator WRI Museum

At the time of going to print, a new permanent exhibition of medical history was in development at the former Infirmary (now the University's City Campus). Extensive collections of medical equipment, documents and uniforms were being selected to go on public display, some for the first time, thanks to a £537,000 grant from the Heritage Lottery Fund.

This exhibition, celebrating the history of medicine, is being created in what was Rushout Ward of the former Worcester Royal Infirmary. The University is working with the George Marshall Medical Museum in the Charles Hastings Education Centre to develop the new exhibition. It will include collections of artefacts from the Infirmary and across Worcestershire, as well as exhibitions celebrating the history of the site. There will be an emphasis on education and participation, with activities to get schoolchildren and members of the public involved.

As one of the first cities outside London to found a voluntary hospital in the 18th century, Worcester has a rich historical legacy charting the development of healthcare provision over the past 300 years. This exciting new exhibition will enable people of all ages to take part in and learn about this extraordinary heritage. The exhibition will include a lively interactive area, which will link the history of medicine to contemporary medical issues such as obesity and mental illness. The exhibition will also celebrate the history of the WRI in the Worcester community, and the stories of people who worked and were treated there during 300 years – including two former members of the WRI Nurses' League, Lucy Ford and Marjorie Tarran.

The new exhibition will be an opportunity to showcase the history of this site, and to engage the community in the history and future of medicine. It will enable curriculum development for schools and Higher Education, offer work placement and volunteering opportunities, and engage further community involvement and outreach.

Visitors to the exhibition, which will be free to enter, will be asked to share their memories and stories of the WRI and will be able to vote and give opinions on today's medical issues, such as stem cell research.

The current George Marshall Medical Museum at the Worcestershire Royal Hospital will remain open, displaying further exhibitions of the City's medical past. The new exhibition in Rushout Ward is due to open in the summer of 2012.

ACKNOWLEDGEMENTS

My grateful thanks go to many people who have helped and advised me, giving encouragement and technical assistance whenever needed, during the years since the idea of putting together these various tales was first suggested.

Firstly, my husband Godfrey has been my "secretary" and critic, patiently typing out each piece, with many alterations and additions.

John Beale, who has expertly guided the manuscript into 'book form' and negotiated with publishers and printers.

Michael McCurdy – Chairman, and the Worcestershire Industrial Archaeology & Local History Society, for their support and encouragement.

Molly and John Pringle and Roger Tapping for expert 'proof reading' and endless correcting and rewriting.

Wendy Cook – Curator of the Worcester Porcelain Museum, for the use of archive material including photographs.

Catriona Smellie – at the time Curator of the George Marshalll Medical Museum, for the use of archive material and photographs, and for a writing a section on the new museum.

David Birtwhistle for very kindly allowing me to use his unique painting of the Worcester Royal Infirmary on the cover.

Staff at the Worcester Records Office for their help.

Committee members of the Worcester Royal Infirmary Nurses League for allowing me to use photographs from the League archive.

Gordon Trueman, Ex-Director of Lea & Perrins for his information on 'Wheeley Lea'.

Duncan Carmichael for his information and use of his photograph – children's ward.

Christine Dorrell, for information regarding the 'boardroom table'.

The Daily Telegraph for permission to use information on Mr. Paul Houghton.

The University of Worcester, for use of information on their website.

SOURCES

The contributions from the following sources are gratefully acknowledged:

COVER
>Painting of Worcester Royal Infirmary by David Birtwhistle by kind permission given by artist and the George Marshall Medical Museum, who own the painting.

EARLY DAYS
>DR. JOHN WALL – "Nash's Worcestershire"
>>W.H.McMenemy – History of Worcester Royal Infirmary.
>>W.H.McMenemy - The Life & Times of Sir Charles Hastings.
>>Joan Lane – Worcester Infirmary in the 18th Century.
>>Archives & Portrait – Worcester Porcelain Museum.
>>Worcester Infirmary Governors' minutes.

>THE ARTICHOKE FIELD
>>Worcester Infirmary Governors' minutes.
>>W.H.McMenemy – History of Worcester Royal Infirmary.
>>City Plan – Worcestershire Records Office.
>>Engraving of Hospital – by Valentine Green.

>CASTLE STREET
>>H.W. Gwillam – People & Places.
>>Picture of Prison – Worcestershire Records Office.
>>Picture of 'death masks' – Author.

>THE HOUSE IN FOREGATE STREET
>>Archives – Worcester Porcelain Museum.
>>Chambers – History of Worcester.
>>W.H.McMenemy – Life & Times of Sir Charles Hastings
>>National Archives – Death of Catherine Wall.

115

Illustration courtesy of Worcester Porcelain Museum.

VICTORIANS

SIR CHARLES HASTINGS

W.H.McMenemy – Life and Times of Sir Charles Hastings.

Portrait – Wellcome Medical Photography Library.

THE JENNY LIND CHAPEL

W.H.McMenemy – History of Worcester Royal Infirmary.

H.W. Gwillam – People & Places.

Archives – Worcester Porcelain Museum.

Illustration of porcelain – Worcester Porcelain Museum – (from Gentleman's Magazine – 1849)

Photograph of Chapel – Mrs D. Kershaw.

NAMING OF THE WARDS

W.H.McMenemy – History of Worcester Royal Infirmary.

Brian Keogh – "The Secret Sauce".

Mr Gordon Truman – past Director of Lee & Perrins.

Pictures – George Marshall Medical Museum.

Wheeley Lea Ward - Portrait of John Wheeley Lea, mayor of Worcester (1849 - 1850) by unknown Artist; collection Worcester City Museums.

THE HOUSE OF INDUSTRY

Research by Mrs M. Clayson – Clinical Tutor.

THE LIFE & TIMES OF Dr. JAMES MANBY GULLY

John Winsor Harcup – The Malvern Water Cure.

Archives – Worcester Porcelain Museum.

IMPROVEMENTS

THE NEW NURSES HOME

Author's own recollections.

W.H.McMenemy – History of Worcester Royal Infirmary.

Photograph – George Marshall Medical Museum.

INFIRMARY EXTENSIONS
> W.H.McMenemy – History of Worcester Royal Infirmary.

H.R.H. THE PRINCE OF WALES – VISIT 1932
> Text & Picture from – The Worcester Advertiser 28th October 1932 from Worcester Porcelain Museum – Archives.

RONKSWOOD HOSPITAL
> Researched by Mrs Muriel Clayson.
> Picture – Mrs Anne Dodsworth

NURSES

NURSE TRAINING IN WORCESTER
> Nursing Mirror 1909.
> W.H.McMenemy – History of Worcester Royal Infirmary.
> Photographs/illustrations of Miss Herbert from George Marshall Medical Museum.
> Photograph of Mulberry House – Author.

STUDENT DAYS
> Author's own memories.
> Picture – Ward scene – George Marshall Medical Museum.
> Prizegiving 1957 Picture – Author centre right – Worcester Royal Infirmary Nurses League.

MATRONS OF WORCESTER ROYAL INFIRMARY
> W.H.McMenemy – History of Worcester Royal Infirmary.

THE COMING OF THE N.H.S.
> Author's original material
> W.H.McMenemy– History of Worcester Royal Infirmary.

PENICILLIN, POLICEMEN & WORCESTER ROYAL INFIRMARY
> Researched by Mrs Muriel Clayson.
> Information from Miss M.E. Tarran SRN. SCM. RCNT – Clinical Tutor.

CHILDREN IN HOSPITAL
Original material by author and Duncan Carmichael
Picture – 1947 – Berrow's Journal.
Picture – George Marshall Medical Museum.
1. Party in Out-patients 1930.
2. On the balcony – Matron Elsie Perry 1931.
THE LAST MATRON – MISS MAY HULME
Oral History project for George Marshall Medical Museum.
Picture – Worcester Royal Infirmary Nurses League Archives.
REMARKABLE CHARACTERS
MR. GEORGE MARSHALL
Text by kind permission of Michael Grundy.
Photograph – George Marshall's retirement in 1971 – Berrows Journal. From left to right:
Mr. P. Houghton – Consultant Surgeon.
Mr. A.C. Clarke – Consultant Orthopaedic Surgeon.
Mr. George Marshall – Senior Consultant Surgeon.
Dr. A. Vickers – Radiologist.
Mr. R.P. Matthews – A/E Consultant.
MISS EVELYN LOUISE HEALEY –
Tribute by niece Miss Joanna Healey.
Picture – presentation to Miss Bowen – Assistant Matron – Berrows Journal. From left to right:
Mr. Duggan – Consultant Surgeon.
Miss Healey – Matron.
Miss Bowen – Assistant Matron.
Mr. Rippier – Hospital Secretary.
Prizegiving 1958 picture – Worcester Royal Infirmary Nurses League. (Matron Healey seated centre and Miss Turner, standing centre back)

SURGEON Lt. Cmd. PAUL HOUGHTON
> Obituary in Daily Telegraph & tribute by P. Bullock.
> Picture – Daily Telegraph – October 23rd 2009.
> Author's own material.

JOHN SMITH – THE MAN – THE NURSE
> A tribute by Jacqui Hughes – Chaplain.
> Personal memories from colleagues
> Picture – Worcester Royal Infirmary Nurses League.

DOCTOR OLAF PULBERG
> Author's own material.

KATHLEEN HARRISON – Elgar's Private Nurse
> Worcester Evening News.

MEMORIES
FRANCES ETHEL BROWN
> Tribute by her niece.
> Photograph – Worcester Royal Infirmary Nurses League.
> Wartime Memories, Autobiographical notes by F.E. Brown.

THE BOARDROOM TABLE
> Information from Mrs Christine Dorrell.
> W.H.McMenemy – History of Worcester Royal Infirmary.
> Picture – George Marshall Medical Museum.

THE "FRIENDS" & THE INFIRMARY BUFFET
> Text and original photograph from Mrs Doris Kershaw.

FORTY THREE YEARS IN PATHOLOGY
> Original material by Colin Legge.
> Picture – Colin Legge.

OPERATING THEATRE 1950'S STYLE
> Author's own material.
> Picture – George Marshall Medical Museum.

GHOSTLY GOINGS ON

Original material by Author and Pauline Shukoi, Hazel Thomas & Linda Randall.

THE BIG MOVE

Original material by Author.

REBIRTH

Original material by Author and Catriona Smellie.

Text and image adapted from University of Worcester website

BIOGRAPHICAL NOTE:

Photograph of author as a student nurse in 1954 – George Marshall Medical Museum.

THE AUTHOR, MIRIAM HARVEY AS A NEW STUDENT NURSE IN 1954

The Author, Miriam Harvey trained at Worcester Royal Infirmary 1954 – 1957 and then spent the next 40 years working in the Operating theatre, specializing in Emergency Surgery.

For 20 years she wrote Historical Articles for the Worcester Royal Infirmary Nurses League magazine, of which she is also the Editor.

Her husband Godfrey ran the Lower Wick Swimming Pool for many years and they have two daughters, both married and living in Worcester.

After retiring in 1996 Miriam trained as a Green Badge Tour Guide in Worcester where she works for "Worcester Walks" and is their Secretary.

Miriam also works, as a volunteer, on two days a week in the archives of the Worcester Porcelain Museum.